The History of Technology

Luca Fraioli

Illustrations by:
G. Bacchin, G. Gaudenzi, I. Stalio

BARRON'S

DoGi

English translation © Copyright 1999
by Barron's Educational Series, Inc.
Original edition © 1999 by DoGi spa, Florence, Italy
Title of original edition: *La storia della tecnologia: L'uomo crea il suo mondo*
Italian edition by: Luca Fraioli
Illustrations by: Giorgio Bacchin, Giacinto Gaudenzi, Ivan Stalio
Editor: Andrea Bachini
Graphic display: Sebastiano Ranchetti
Page make-up: Antonio Tucci
Iconographic researcher: Katherine Carlson Forden

English translation by Venetia Scalo

All inquiries should be addressed to:
Barron's Educational Series, Inc.
250 Wireless Boulevard
Hauppauge, NY 11788
http://www.barronseduc.com

Library of Congress Catalog Card No. 98-76193

International Standard Book No. 0-7641-0945-6

Printed in Italy
9 8 7 6 5 4 3 2 1

Table of Contents

A VERY SLOW START

Two and a half million years ago, in Africa, a hominid chipped at stone to sharpen it: thus, the first tool was born. The next great turning point in history came about ten thousand years ago with the Neolithic Revolution: successful farming and herding of animals.

Gradually pre-Neolithic human's ancestors stood up on their hind limbs and began to walk. This detachment from the ground resulted in some very important changes: the position of the skull on the spine, the profile of the face, the development of the brain, and the formation of language. But the development of increasingly refined technologies would not have been possible if all these had not also been accompanied by the evolution of the hand. Endowed with the extraordinary facility of hands, humans distinguished themselves from other living beings by a capacity to think, produce, and use aids made by these very hands: utensils. Naturally the hand has had a long evolution. From the time that human's erect position freed them from sustaining the weight of their bodies while crawling on the

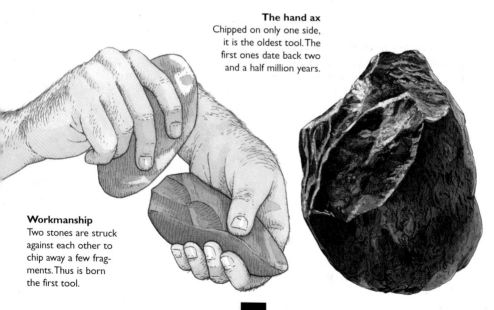

The hand ax
Chipped on only one side, it is the oldest tool. The first ones date back two and a half million years.

Workmanship
Two stones are struck against each other to chip away a few fragments. Thus is born the first tool.

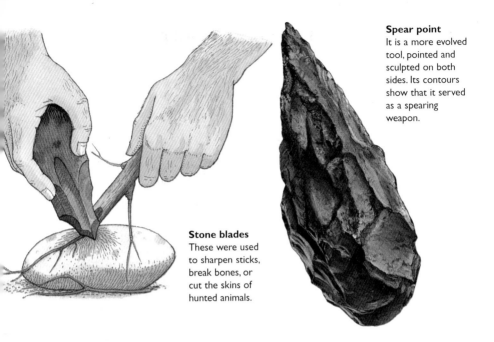

Spear point
It is a more evolved tool, pointed and sculpted on both sides. Its contours show that it served as a spearing weapon.

Stone blades
These were used to sharpen sticks, break bones, or cut the skins of hunted animals.

ground, the hand began the long evolution that enabled it to perform great exertions and detailed manipulations. Almost all that we know about early humans comes to us from the study of their first tools: chipped stones.

Over the course of two and a half million years, humans went from crude pebbles to fine points of arrows chiseled from flint. Many hundreds of thousands of years separate the chopper from the two-sided implement called the ax.

But which hominid first had a brain that was complex enough to conceive of and construct tools of stone? Anthropologists have called this hominid *Homo habilis*.

Homo habilis appeared in Africa about two and a half million years ago. In places where this species lived, pebbles chipped to form a cutting edge have been found. Such tools could be used to cut into the skin of dead animals, making them easier to eat. History's first invention therefore had an immediate practical consequence: an increase in animal meat consumed by *Homo habilis*.

Homo erectus and *Homo sapiens*

However, it is *Homo erectus* who is most important in the beginning stages of the history of technology. The fossil remains of these hominids have an age of between one and a half million and two hundred thousand years and have been found in Africa, Asia, and Europe, which is to say that *Homo erectus* dominated the world for more than a million years.

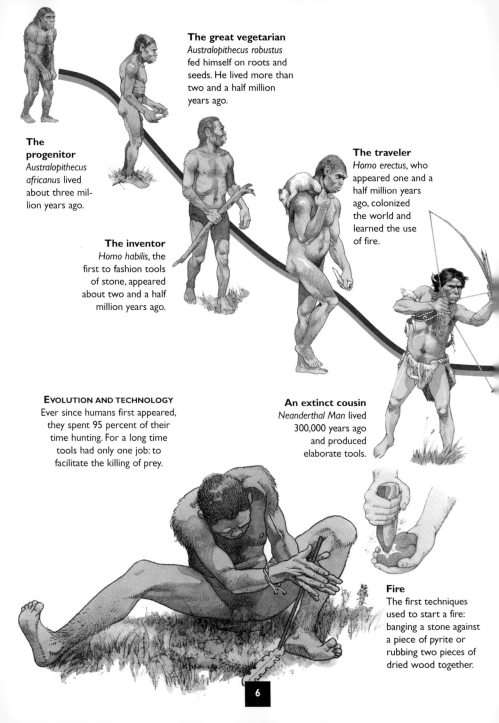

The great vegetarian
Australopithecus robustus fed himself on roots and seeds. He lived more than two and a half million years ago.

The progenitor
Australopithecus africanus lived about three million years ago.

The traveler
Homo erectus, who appeared one and a half million years ago, colonized the world and learned the use of fire.

The inventor
Homo habilis, the first to fashion tools of stone, appeared about two and a half million years ago.

EVOLUTION AND TECHNOLOGY
Ever since humans first appeared, they spent 95 percent of their time hunting. For a long time tools had only one job: to facilitate the killing of prey.

An extinct cousin
Neanderthal Man lived 300,000 years ago and produced elaborate tools.

Fire
The first techniques used to start a fire: banging a stone against a piece of pyrite or rubbing two pieces of dried wood together.

The secrets of their success were their erect position in walking, a much more developed brain than that of their predecessors, and a greater aptitude in making more sophisticated and diversified new tools. Furthermore, it is assumed that it was none other than *Homo erectus*, about one million years ago, who conquered fire, transforming it from a source of danger to a means of defense against animals and cold.

The oldest fossils relating to *Homo sapiens*, the Neanderthals, are traced to between 100,000 and 200,000 years ago and have been recovered in Africa, Europe, and Asia. *Homo sapiens sapiens*, ancestors of all modern people, replaced the Neanderthals. Leaving their African homeland, they colonized Europe and Asia.

The period between 37,000 and 10,000 years ago was characterized by innovations in making tools, ornaments, and weapons such as the spear, whose tip might have been of incised bone.

The direct ancestor
More than 100,000 years ago, *Homo sapiens sapiens* made their appearance in Africa.

Complex tools
These were made by tying wooden handles to chipped rocks.

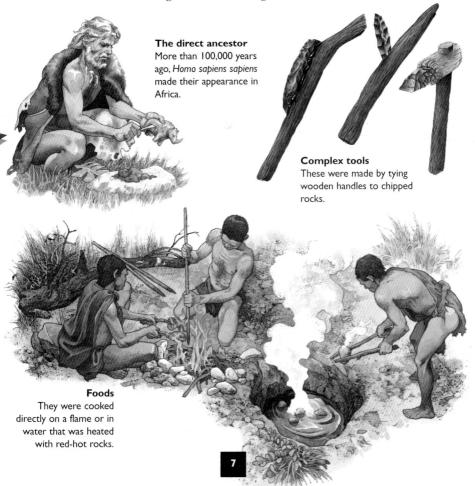

Foods
They were cooked directly on a flame or in water that was heated with red-hot rocks.

THE FIRST SETTLEMENTS
They sprang up close to
sources of water, indispensable
for agriculture and cattle
raising. The villages consisted
of one or more huts, often
built above the ground
to avoid flood.

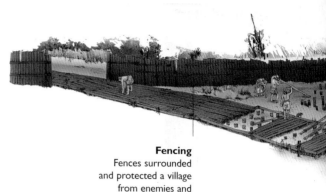

Fencing
Fences surrounded
and protected a village
from enemies and
animals. The dog
was the first animal
that people
domesticated.

Plowing
They learned that
moving the soil
would facilitate the
sowing of plants.

The techniques of stone-cutting became so refined as to permit *Homo sapiens* to produce blades as fine as a leaf. And while the working of items made of flint had only a practical goal, objects made of bone and horn assumed the characteristics of true works of art.

The historical era that dates from the appearance of *Homo erectus* to the proliferation of *Homo sapiens sapiens*, when stone became the principal material for tools and utensils, has been given the name of the Old Stone Age or the Paleolithic Age. The first tools were used to kill prey and cut up their meat and hides. The tools were used by the entire community, whose survival was dependent upon hunting or scavenging animals to eat, and gathering wild seeds along with edible fruits. Such a diet and way of life shaped the social

The roof
Consisting of two slopes, it was made of straw or rushes.

The first boats
Men first learned to straddle a tree trunk and later to hollow it out to make room for baggage.

Ditches
They were made of clay, and refuse was deposited there. They have been most useful to archaeologists in reconstructing the habits of ancient inhabitants.

The first huts
They were lake dwellings supported by large stakes driven into the ground. The walls were made of intertwined branches held together with straw and clay.

First storage bins
Gathered grains and vegetables were preserved in holes dug into rocks.

organization of early mankind.

The community of hunter-gatherers often experienced a shortage of food and lived under the constant threat of famine. It was forced to look for food, and group members had to dedicate all of their energies to finding food; The first communities of *Homo sapiens* were nomads, and within this community there was no significant diversification of labor.

No one would have survived pursuing any work other than hunting, such as, for example, the production of stone utensils bartered for food found by one's companions.

The neolithic revolution

The last glaciation ended about 10,000 years ago. The glacial icecaps receded, the level of the rivers rose, the climate became more mild, and on the continents, forests replaced the steppe and tundra. At this time a change began, gradual but with revolutionary repercussions in the living habits of humans. This phenomenon has been named the Neolithic Revolution: from hunters and gatherers people became farmers and herders. It was a decisive phase in the development of humanity: those who plowed fields or fenced in animals stopped, abandoned their nomadic lives, and constructed permanent settlements. Sustenance derived from the earth characterized practically all of humanity up to the time of the Industrial Revolution of

THE CITY AND THE FIELDS
The first cities arose during the fourth millenium B.C.: simple groups of houses made of clay bricks allowed to dry in the sun and placed upon each other without the use of mortar.

the eighteenth century. After this revolution, science and technology provided the means for an even more decisive achievement.

Today many areas of the world still base their economy exclusively on agriculture. There are still some people, such as Australian aborigines or the Inuit, who live by hunting and gathering. Why did humans at a certain moment become herdsmen and farmers? Why did they decide to stop building villages?

Implements
Scythes for reaping and a mortar to grind wheat.

The plow
Made completely of wood, it dug shallow furrows and could not be used on heavy ground.

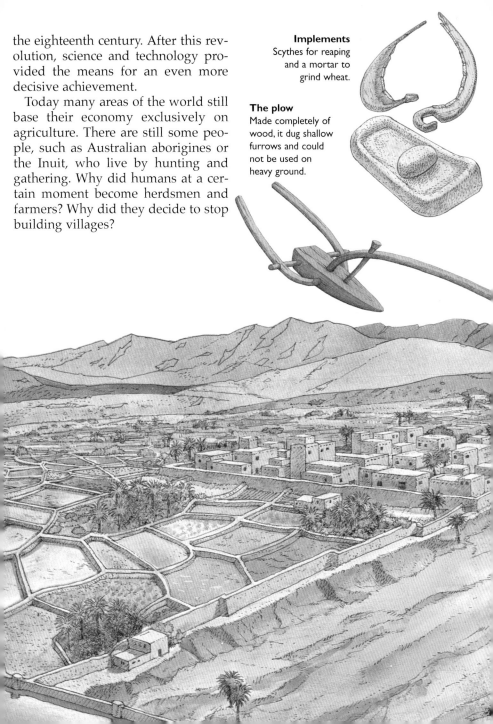

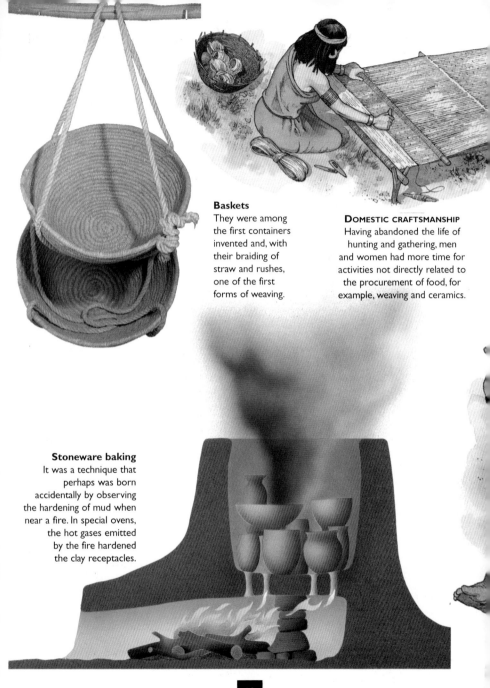

Baskets
They were among the first containers invented and, with their braiding of straw and rushes, one of the first forms of weaving.

DOMESTIC CRAFTSMANSHIP
Having abandoned the life of hunting and gathering, men and women had more time for activities not directly related to the procurement of food, for example, weaving and ceramics.

Stoneware baking
It was a technique that perhaps was born accidentally by observing the hardening of mud when near a fire. In special ovens, the hot gases emitted by the fire hardened the clay receptacles.

Weaving
The spinning wheel and the loom made the production of the first fabrics possible.

Potter's wheels
Spirally mounted, they facilitated the production of very simple vases.

A warmer and more humid climate favored new crops.

The so-called Fertile Crescent—the area of the Middle East that extends from the Mediterranean coast to the Mesopotamian plains of the Tigris and Euphrates rivers and pushes down to the Persian Gulf—became populated with fertile plants and domesticable animals. Other areas—such as the Indus Valley, the Nile River Valley, and the Chinese Yellow River region—offered the same advantages. During the Neolithic Period, almost simultaneously in various parts of the planet, crops were planted and animals were domesticated to obtain milk, blood, meat, or hides. New instruments, obtained by using honed rocks ("Neolithic," in fact, means "age of the new stone"), among which were the first rudimentary plows, made tilling more effective and food surpluses available.

The birth of craftsmanship

Advances from the Fertile Crescent made during the Neolithic Period spread throughout southern Europe, Egypt, and Western Asia. Agriculture slowly made its way north and northwest and toward the western side of the Mediterranean. The food surplus led to a gradual increase in population. About 3500 B.C. comfortable and solid houses were first constructed, and cities began to be inhabited not only by farmers but also by priests, administrators, clerks, and artisans.

In those first cities artisan activities sprang up including grinding of wheat, baking of clay containers, weaving and dyeing of fabrics, and distillation of drinks.

Mines
They took advantage of the subterranean portion of mineral veins that emerged on the surface.

Smelting
With bellows made of hides, air was pumped to raise the temperature of the oven.

Some of these techniques were the result of continuous efforts made over a long period of time; others arose almost by accident, such as the production of pottery.

It is likely that rudimentary forms of weaving had been noted before the Neolithic Period, but proven examples of fabric weaving date to 6000 B.C., when women, who were beginning to have more time at their disposal, began to apply their knowledge of spinning and braiding threads to the construc-

tion of baskets and mats. While the baskets themselves did not change drastically, the weaving process itself made continual progress toward the invention of the loom.

In conjunction with these new activities, the lifestyles of the inhabitants of the first cities changed, improved by the availability of clothing, earthenware, and new utensils. The availability of these new goods greatly stimulated commerce between different communities, as archaeological evidence relating

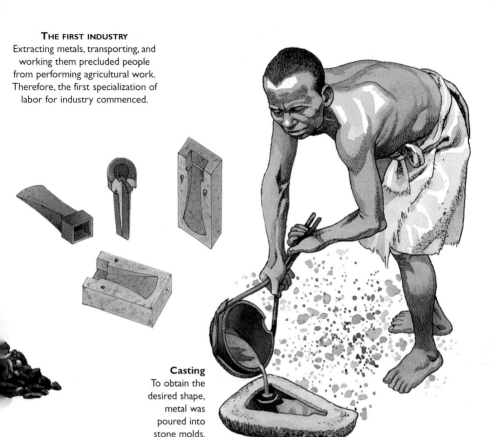

Casting
To obtain the desired shape, metal was poured into stone molds.

to the last phase of the Neolithic Period confirms.

Metalworking

About 4000 B.C. men learned to extract and work subterranean metals to manufacture utensils and weapons. It was an innovation without precedent: a chipped stone can cut more efficiently than a metal blade can, but metal lasts longer, can be sharpened repeatedly, and, above all, can be molded into a desired shape.

The first metal to be worked was copper: copper mines have been found in Egypt, in the Sinai Desert. It was clear very early on that, despite its advantages over utensils of stone or wood, copper was a metal that was too soft to make effective blades: the first smiths therefore began to fuse copper with other metals to obtain a more durable alloy, bronze.

Thus various types of bronze became widespread, some of which contained, in addition to copper, lead or arsenic. But the kind of bronze that enjoyed the greatest success was obtained by combining ten parts of copper with one part of tin. Ironworking, dating to approximately 1500 B.C., was of maximum importance toward evolution more for the production of tools than of weapons. Iron proved to be, in fact, ideal for the production of pliers, saws, and anvils.

The lathe
Rotary motion allowed clay vases to be produced more rapidly. The use of the wheel in the production of pottery became popular about 3500 B.C.

The wheel

Among the innovations encountered thus far, there is an omission that baffles us: the wheel. Our prehistoric ancestors learned early enough to shape stone, to control fire, to extract metals, to cultivate plants and breed animals, but they understood only about 6000 years ago the importance and usefulness of rotary motion. Today the wheel seems to us a banal object, but its discovery and its first uses were nothing of the sort. Indeed, the first potter's wheel appeared in Mesopotamia between 3500 and 3000 B.C., while the first cart on wheels didn't appear until almost another thousand years. Among the first to move on wheeled vehicles were probably Sumerian soldiers, the ancient people that inhabited Mesopotamia.

The advent of the wheel revolutionized the method of fighting and, obviously, the method of transportation.

The sled
It was the most widely used means of transportation before the cart, used on snow, steppes, and sandy deserts.

The evolution of the wheel
The first ones were solid discs of wood. They were made lighter when spokes were invented.

Carpentry
Egyptian hatchets, saws, drills, and chisels—necessary for the construction of boats and carts.

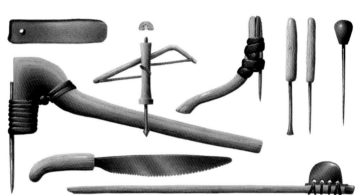

The sail
The Egyptians were the first to use it to sail upstream on the Nile.

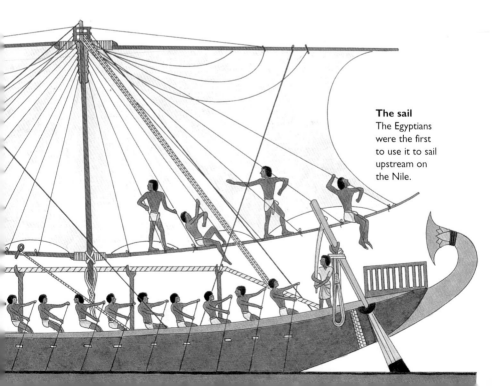

Indeed, until then the only means of transportation on land was the sled dragged by animals: once the wheel was invented, inventing the cart required nothing more than mounting a sled with an axel on a couple of wheels.

In any event, wheeled vehicles, a symbol of prestige and power, remained the privilege of a few, so much so that some carts were buried in graves alongside their owners: it is this very custom that has allowed the preservation of some examples to this day.

THE GREAT BUILDERS
Egypt's large pyramids were built without using wheeled vehicles. Great slabs of stone were hauled on inclined planes of packed earth.

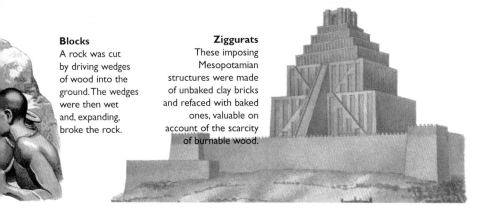

Blocks
A rock was cut by driving wedges of wood into the ground. The wedges were then wet and, expanding, broke the rock.

Ziggurats
These imposing Mesopotamian structures were made of unbaked clay bricks and refaced with baked ones, valuable on account of the scarcity of burnable wood.

From prehistory to history

As the basic needs of humanity were increasingly met, more complex forms of social organization were devised. With the development of science, astronomy in particular, of political forms that culminated in the formation of state governments, and of an organized system of signs and symbols, such as writing, humanity left prehistory behind and entered into history.

The city-state first arose in Mesopotamia. The great rivers there fostered high-yield agriculture, which required a disciplined, organized labor force. This in turn favored the establishment of centralized civil governments that could make laws.

The brickmaking technique
A mixture of clay and straw, marked with a wooden stencil and left to dry in the sun.

After the fourth millenium B.C., the Sumerians and Egyptians divided themselves into new social classes: artisans, scribes, and bureaucrats were employed to administer the goods of the king or the pharaoh. It was the Sumerians who addressed the need for a system of standard signs with which to count objects: thus were born the first forms of writing, small symbols engraved on clay tablets, an instrument so exceptional for the transmission of knowledge from one generation to the next that historians credit that exact moment, when writing was born, as the turning point from prehistory to true history.

But the great civilizations of the past have, above all, left a legacy of their magnificent and imposing buildings: their dimensions point to a great innovation in the construction of edifices. In Mesopotamia there was a scarcity of stone, and wood was also rare. The Egyptians had an abundant stone supply at their disposal in the valley of the Nile. Construction techniques were based on very simple principles: hauling on rollers, the inclined plane, the water level. The Sumerians, continuing to use sun-dried clay bricks, invented bearing walls often of more than 8 feet in size and produced brick pillars to support their great temples. The Egyptians built pyramids and temples under the direction of priest-architects who were experts in mathematics as well as astronomy: the arrangement of many of their buildings calls to mind, in fact, that of some constellations.

EGYPTIAN AGRICULTURE
The behavior of the Nile regulated agriculture and the calendar.
The year was divided into three seasons: (1) the flooding, (2) the receding (recession) of the waters, (3) the dry spell.

Villages
They were built upon hills, protected from floods.

Palm trees
Wheat and barley crops were often overshadowed by date palm trees.

1. Flooding
In the month of July, the Nile overflowed, replenished top soil, and flooded the farmlands.

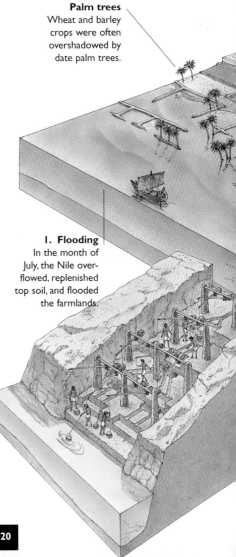

Slabs of stone were cut by expert stonecutters and set in their proper place by groups of peasants, who were available by the rotation of the farming season. The Egyptians had, in fact, developed the most perfectly irrigated agricultural system that existed in antiquity. From a desert land, in an arid and inhospitable climate, they profited from the Nile's regular floods from the rains that fed it at its source in the faraway plateaus. They harnessed the floods by constructing dams and channels: in this way the gained control over the whims of nature.

The highlands
Since they did not receive water from the overflowing river, they were irrigated by channels using the shadoof system.

Sowing and harvesting
They occurred after the waters recede and before the next flood.

3. The dry spell
Between October and June, irrigation of the land was needed.

The shadoof
A system to irrigate lands untouched by the flood. The counterweight lifts the water-filled goatskin to the other end of the rod.

2. The receding of the waters
After it occurred in October, a very fertile marsh remained.

HIGH CULTURE WITH LITTLE TECHNOLOGY

The Greeks and Romans dominated the Mediterranean world for centuries, and their culture has left its mark on the world of today. While they did not make major technological advances, they were brilliant architects and capable engineers, producing works that we still admire today.

The period between the eighth century B.C., approximately when the first Greek *pòleis* (city-states) were born, and the fifth century A.D., when the Western Roman Empire fell, is defined as the Classical Age. During this entire span of time, the foundations of what we know as Western culture or civilization were established in many fields, from philosophy to law, and from art to literature and religion.

There is a great contrast between the achievements of the Greeks and the Romans in religion, philosophy, political and natural sciences, poetry, literature, and scientific investigation and their modest contributions to the progress of technology. With the exception of military and building techniques, classical antiquity knew above all how to use already existing ideas, tools, and instruments. Why? Some historians have singled out the practice of slavery to be the cause of

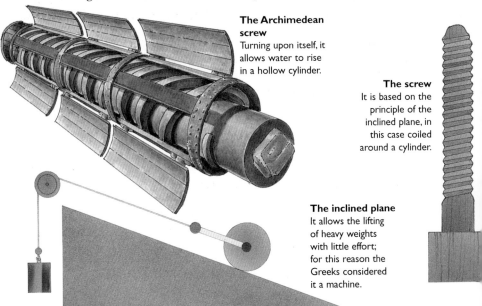

The Archimedean screw
Turning upon itself, it allows water to rise in a hollow cylinder.

The screw
It is based on the principle of the inclined plane, in this case coiled around a cylinder.

The inclined plane
It allows the lifting of heavy weights with little effort; for this reason the Greeks considered it a machine.

The lever
Archimedes formulated its principle. A force applied far from the fulcrum is equal to a greater force applied closer to it.

Ctesibius's clock
Drop by drop the water level is raised and so is the needle.

the technological backwardness of the Greek and Roman world: relying on the low-paying work performed by slaves, the Greeks and Romans did not feel the need to create innovations for people who plowed the fields or split rocks and boulders.

According to the Latin writer Lucius Annaeus Seneca (who lived during the first century A.D.), many of the inventions of his time were the work of slaves, the only ones who took an interest in practical innovation. A strong agricultural economy and, in the case of Rome, the domination of other peoples, were two reasons for the lack of "curiosity" within the classical world. The practical achievements were more or less restricted to the fields of information processing and transmission. We think of the creation of money, stenography, and geometry. Each society improves upon the knowledge in the fields that are most important to its preservation and development. The Romans, who were the rulers of the largest empire of all European antiquity, were innovative in the art of war and in military and civil engineering.

Hellenic technology

About 1500 B.C. the Hittites of Anatolia made a fundamental contribution to iron metallurgy, and popularized it throughout the entire Aegean. They perfected the extraction techniques for smelting, the process of separating rock and metal by raising the temperature of metal until it becomes liquid but leaves the rock behind.

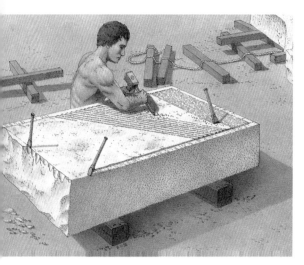

Stone temples
Their construction was inspired by wooden structures, embedded with marble rafters. The most famous Greek temple is the Parthenon of Athens, commissioned by Pericles between 447 and 432 B.C.

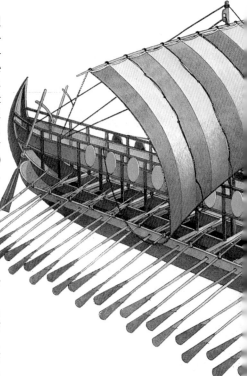

The Greeks also recognized the importance that individual components could contribute to the efficiency of machines: the lever, the pulley, the wedge, the screw, and the gear. Archimedes, the most famous of Greek inventors, who lived in Syracuse between about 290 and 211 B.C., is considered the inventor of many of these devices. Ctesibius (170–117 B.C.) and Heron (circa the first century B.C.), of Alexandria, Egypt, constructed pumps, air and hydraulic organs, and even a primitive steam-powered car. But their innovations were applied primarily to war implements and ingenious devices, designed to be admired rather than to serve a practical purpose.

Even the great Greek temples that we still admire today were not a product of significant technological innovation. The oldest structures were built of crude bricks and were sustained by a

wooden framework, not very different from those of the last phase of the Neolithic Period.

Greece, however, was a country rich in a rock that was suitable for construction, so rich, in fact, that it was nicknamed the marble peninsula. This marble became the most widely used material in the building of temples and palaces from 500 B.C. The most popular stone was Pentelic marble, extracted from a mountain just north of Athens. The Parthenon and most of the public buildings of classical Athens were made of this marble. Its excellent quality permitted Greek architects and sculptors to make refinements unique in the history of architecture.

Greeks also made original contributions to navigation. The ships described by Homer in the *Iliad* and the *Odyssey* were constructed using the same technique that is used today for most wooden ships: the keel, the backbone of the hull, was, for instance, already fully developed, while the master carpenters of northern Europe would wait many centuries to adopt it. As far back as the sixth century B.C., a fine distinction between Greek warships and merchant ships existed. The former were long-keeled, equipped with a rectangular sail and various levels of oars; arm muscle provided the craft with its push in the absence of wind or when sailing against the wind. Merchant ships, on the other hand, were rounded and, lacking oars, traveled only by wind. Merchants would have been unable to sustain the costs incurred by a team of rowers.

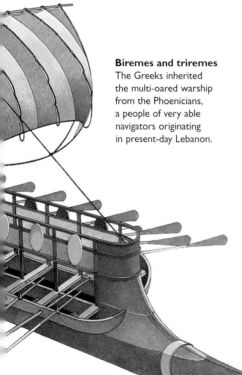

Biremes and triremes
The Greeks inherited the multi-oared warship from the Phoenicians, a people of very able navigators originating in present-day Lebanon.

An empire of engineers

Like the Greek civilization, the Roman civilization did not make extraordinary technological strides, and the few that did emerge were all concentrated in the military sector and public works. Rome grew with each successive war. By 300 B.C. it controlled much of southern Italy; in 241 it ousted the Carthaginians from Sicily. By the beginning of the second century B.C., Rome was already a great Mediterranean power. Roman soldiers did invent new war machines, but more often they improved upon those already introduced by the Greeks. They were, however, unsurpassed masters of the art of war: the discipline and organization of their troops on the battlefield were their best weapons. Nevertheless, the prestige and popularity of the Roman state rested mainly on its development of public works. In the first century A.D., the paved streets of Rome, its sewers, its aqueducts, and its systems of fireproofing could have competed with those of the European capitals of the nineteenth century.

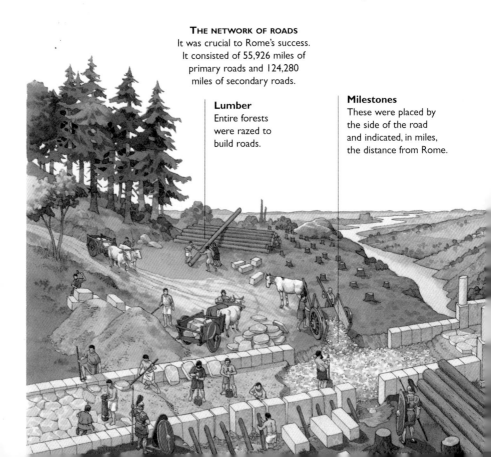

THE NETWORK OF ROADS
It was crucial to Rome's success. It consisted of 55,926 miles of primary roads and 124,280 miles of secondary roads.

Lumber
Entire forests were razed to build roads.

Milestones
These were placed by the side of the road and indicated, in miles, the distance from Rome.

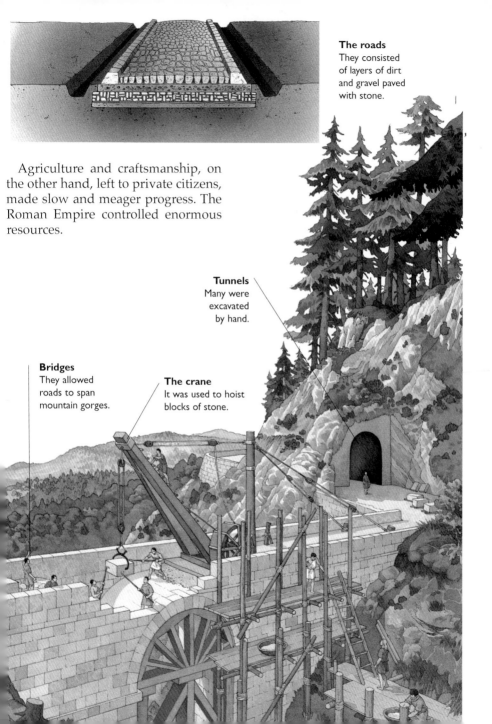

The roads
They consisted of layers of dirt and gravel paved with stone.

Agriculture and craftsmanship, on the other hand, left to private citizens, made slow and meager progress. The Roman Empire controlled enormous resources.

Tunnels
Many were excavated by hand.

Bridges
They allowed roads to span mountain gorges.

The crane
It was used to hoist blocks of stone.

The network of roads was indispensable to the Roman army, for the inspection of the empire, and for transportation via land. The cost of transporting heavy or bulky merchandise doubled every 100 miles. Development of infrastructures depended on the improvement of old or the use of new construction techniques and materials: masonry in concrete (sand and gravel mixed with water and cement) was already known in Anatolia, but the Romans perfected it. Cement became typical of Roman construction: it was waterproof and therefore ideal for the construction of the domes and vaults of thermal baths. Among the building stones most often used was travertine, a limestone extracted from deposits found in the

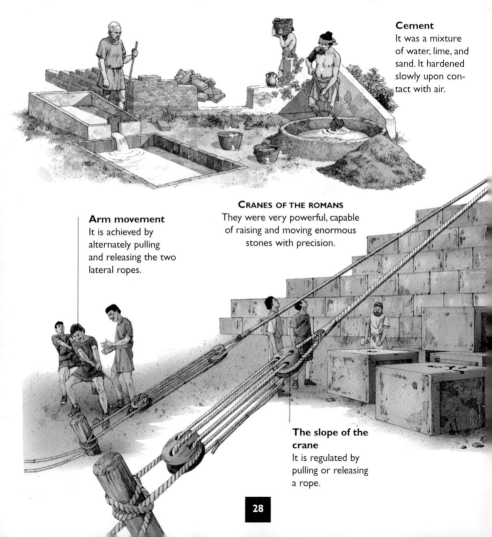

Cement
It was a mixture of water, lime, and sand. It hardened slowly upon contact with air.

Arm movement
It is achieved by alternately pulling and releasing the two lateral ropes.

CRANES OF THE ROMANS
They were very powerful, capable of raising and moving enormous stones with precision.

The slope of the crane
It is regulated by pulling or releasing a rope.

valley of the Tiber, and tufa, a con-
glomerate of volcanic origin.

Clay bricks were also used successfully. Until the first emperor, Augustus Caesar (27 B.C.), they were allowed
to dry in the sun; later they were
baked in specially built kilns.

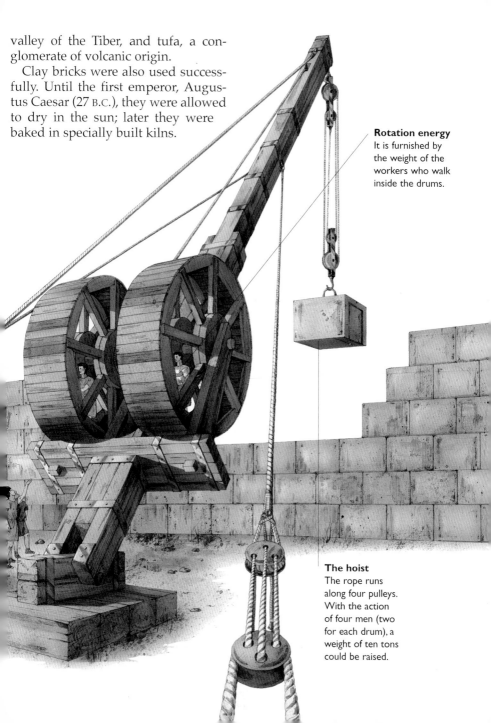

Rotation energy
It is furnished by
the weight of the
workers who walk
inside the drums.

The hoist
The rope runs
along four pulleys.
With the action
of four men (two
for each drum), a
weight of ten tons
could be raised.

The birth of the empire also signaled the triumph of marble.

It has been written that Augustus "found Rome made of bricks and left it made of marble." Marble was used to build new structures and to reface those already existing in brick.

The Arch

One of the most frequently recur-ring architectural elements in Roman buildings and one that they used with the greatest expertise is the arch. The Romans learned how to construct arches from the Etruscans. They sub-sequently perfected the technique, applying it to bridges and aqueducts. They also achieved a high level of achievement in the two natural evolu-tions of the arch: the vault and the dome.

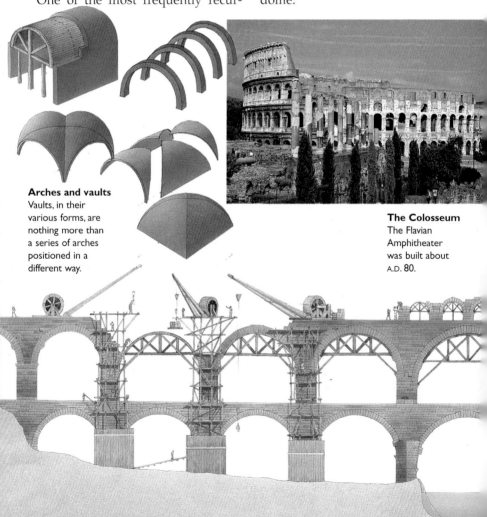

Arches and vaults
Vaults, in their various forms, are nothing more than a series of arches positioned in a different way.

The Colosseum
The Flavian Amphitheater was built about A.D. 80.

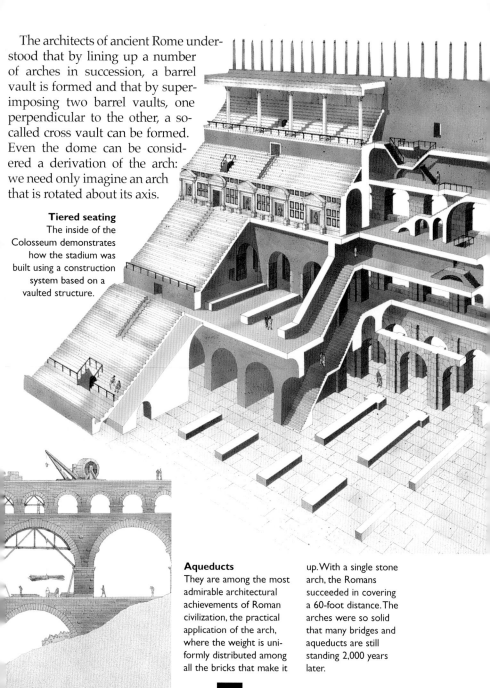

The architects of ancient Rome understood that by lining up a number of arches in succession, a barrel vault is formed and that by superimposing two barrel vaults, one perpendicular to the other, a so-called cross vault can be formed. Even the dome can be considered a derivation of the arch: we need only imagine an arch that is rotated about its axis.

Tiered seating
The inside of the Colosseum demonstrates how the stadium was built using a construction system based on a vaulted structure.

Aqueducts
They are among the most admirable architectural achievements of Roman civilization, the practical application of the arch, where the weight is uniformly distributed among all the bricks that make it up. With a single stone arch, the Romans succeeded in covering a 60-foot distance. The arches were so solid that many bridges and aqueducts are still standing 2,000 years later.

The Romans constructed imposing domes: the most celebrated is that of the Pantheon (built about A.D. 120), which has a diameter of 141 feet and 12 inches. The first aqueduct to bring drinkable water to the city was built in 300 B.C. and was completely underground. Claudius's enormous aqueduct, completed during the Imperial Age, required 14 years of work and 40,000 carts filled with blocks of tufa each year.

But the Romans did not supply only the capital with drinkable water.

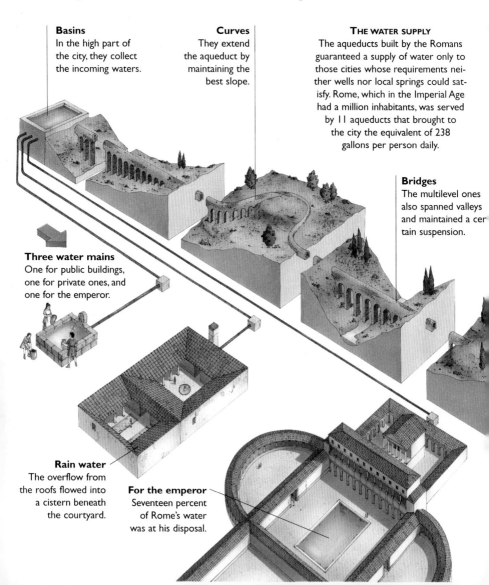

Basins
In the high part of the city, they collect the incoming waters.

Curves
They extend the aqueduct by maintaining the best slope.

THE WATER SUPPLY
The aqueducts built by the Romans guaranteed a supply of water only to those cities whose requirements neither wells nor local springs could satisfy. Rome, which in the Imperial Age had a million inhabitants, was served by 11 aqueducts that brought to the city the equivalent of 238 gallons per person daily.

Bridges
The multilevel ones also spanned valleys and maintained a certain suspension.

Three water mains
One for public buildings, one for private ones, and one for the emperor.

Rain water
The overflow from the roofs flowed into a cistern beneath the courtyard.

For the emperor
Seventeen percent of Rome's water was at his disposal.

We can still see long lines of multi-leveled arches in many parts of France, Spain, Italy, and Egypt. The portion of the Roman Empire that is today Germany had large aqueducts at Cologne, Bonn, Mainz, and Trier.

Despite the great attention that the Romans paid to water and its use, they did not excel at employing it as a source of energy. They knew the water mill well, but they built only a few and made greater use of mills powered by men or animals.

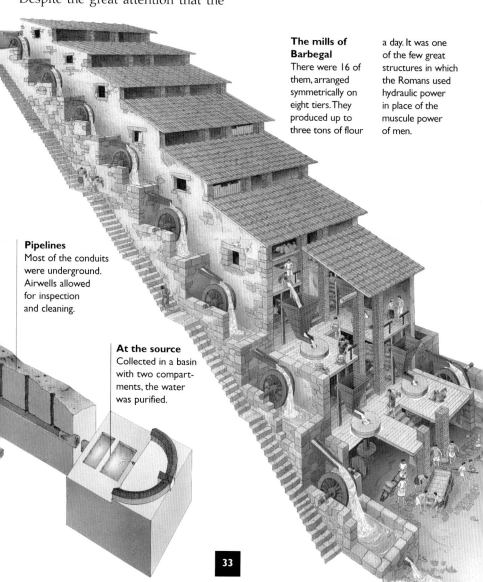

The mills of Barbegal
There were 16 of them, arranged symmetrically on eight tiers. They produced up to three tons of flour a day. It was one of the few great structures in which the Romans used hydraulic power in place of the muscule power of men.

Pipelines
Most of the conduits were underground. Airwells allowed for inspection and cleaning.

At the source
Collected in a basin with two compartments, the water was purified.

THE DECLINE AND RISE OF EUROPE

The end of the Classical Age meant that Europe entered into a period of decline. Other cultures, like Asia, surpassed them in technological progress. Their inventions, however, were adopted by the Europeans, who, beginning in the eleventh century, began a new phase of expansion.

At the end of the fifth century, the great population shifts occurred because of the Barbarian Invasions, which turned the social and political framework of the Graeco-Roman civilization upside down, and led to the gradual cultural decline of Europe, a process that lasted almost six centuries. The birth of this Dark Age or Middle Age is generally thought to coincide with the fall of the Western Roman Empire in A.D. 476. After this date, many of the major centers of classical knowledge began to wane: in 529 the Byzantine emperor Justinian ordered the closing of the Academy and the Lyceum of Athens; in 641 the Arabs destroyed what was left of the museum in Alexandria. Much of the cultural heritage of antiquity was destroyed, and roads, bridges, aqueducts, villas, and the very foundation of urban civilization fell into ruin.

What ensued was a transition to when even emperors were not acquainted

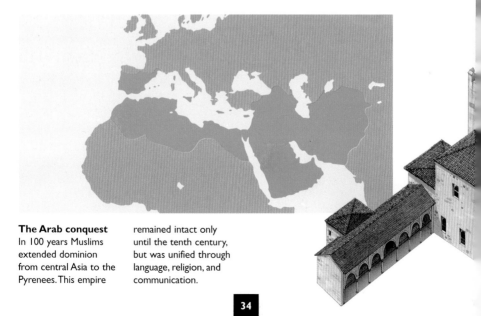

The Arab conquest
In 100 years Muslims extended dominion from central Asia to the Pyrenees. This empire remained intact only until the tenth century, but was unified through language, religion, and communication.

with the Classical past. Only the Christian Church kept learning alive. For example, Charlemagne, whose empire was the first to restore a partial political unity to the European peoples, in 800, barely knew how to read and write.

The Arabs

From the eighth century until the thirteenth, the true heir of the classical civilization was the Islamic world. It dominated the area from Arabia in the Middle East through North Africa to Spain. Islamic technology thus became a synthesis of diverse technical cultures; the Hellenic and Roman culture merged with contributions from central Asia, India, Africa, and even the Far East.

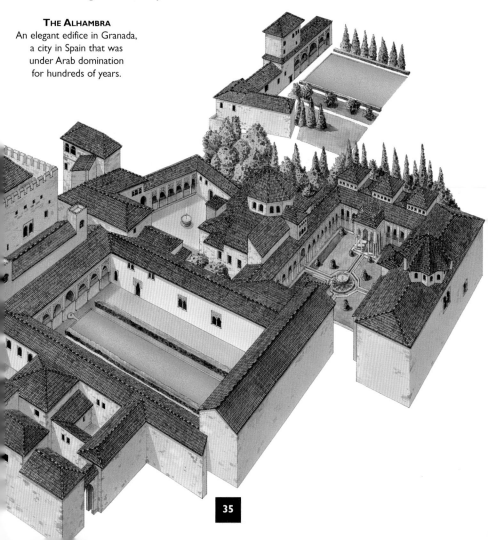

THE ALHAMBRA
An elegant edifice in Granada, a city in Spain that was under Arab domination for hundreds of years.

The Moslems archived the knowledge they collected in large libraries. Even before these efficient techniques were perfected, Moslems gave life to new scientific achievements: numerals—henceforth known as Arabic numbers—the invention of algebra, advances in astronomy, the discovery of alkalis in chemistry. The Arabs also knew how to translate their scientific knowledge into technological achievements: the study of chemistry led them to the production of naphtha, a fireproof derivative of petroleum, and to the establishment of perfume and acid industries. In addition, they excelled in mixing colors that they used to dye fabrics in order to improve their quality. Islam's contribution to the textile industry is aptly demonstrated in the names of many fabrics: damask originated in the Syrian city of Damascus, muslin from Mosul in Iraq, and fustian from Fustat, in Egypt. Also attributed to the Arabs is the invention of the lateen sail, a tool of decisive importance in navigation. The Moslems distinguished themselves in the nutritional field by their cultivation of sugarcane. They also introduced to European tables foods of Asian origin such as rice, oranges, and artichokes.

But the Far Eastern item that had the greatest impact was paper. Tradition has it that the Arabs discovered it thanks to Chinese artisans captured during the conquest of Samarkand, in 753.

After the twelfth century the Arab world made less technological

The lateen sail
It was the first "trimmed sail," that is, one capable of taking wind on both sides and therefore of allowing ships to travel more rapidly.

DYE
The colored fabrics produced in Arab nations became immensely popular in both European and Asian markets. They were often richly colored and decorated with images of living beings, despite the Moslem prohibition on producing such representations.

progress. This was primarily due to a series of military defeats, which resulted in its loss of Spain from the Mongo invasions in the East.

China

Until the fifteenth century, the Chinese were much more proficient at utilizing scientific knowledge than the Europeans.

Dyes
They were extracted from the roots of plants, mineral sub-stances, and insects. The extraction proce-dures were jealously guarded.

The vats
Coloring powders were dissolved in them. Fabrics were first immersed in the liquid and then hung out to dry in the sun.

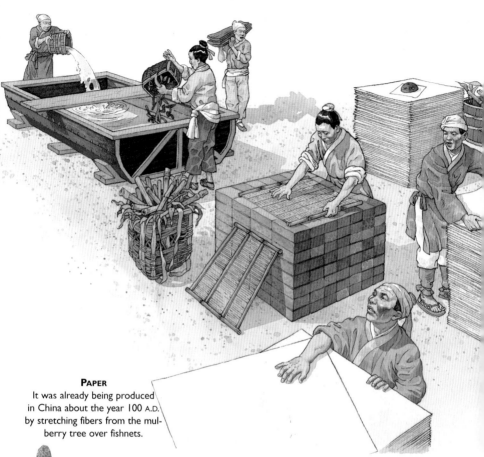

PAPER
It was already being produced in China about the year 100 A.D. by stretching fibers from the mulberry tree over fishnets.

Paper was invented before the year 100 A.D. and spread rapidly throughout the Orient, but it was only one of many technological achievements from a civilization that had been flourishing since 2000 B.C.

Since the survival of the population was tied to the beneficial, as well as the devastating, floods of the Yellow River, the first important gains made by the Chinese were in the field of hydraulic engineering. Improved control of the flooding techniques of the countryside permitted an enormous expansion of rice cultivation in the southern regions. The Chinese constructed new tools such as the iron plow and sowing machines. Although blast furnaces were developed in the Middle East before China, the Chinese built them to cast iron 1500 years before the Europeans. They knew how to produce porcelain and work brass. About 100

B.C. they discovered that magnets point in the direction of the North Pole, taking the first step toward the invention of the compass.

The first text printed on paper appeared in the ninth century. Probably around the same time gunpowder was invented, in the eleventh century, rudimentary rockets were used as weapons in battle. In the fourteenth century, China reached its stride in terms of industrialization. And yet it did not succeed in becoming a dominant world power. A tendency toward conservative Confucian values and isolation dominated the ruling classes. With the Kangxi emperor the Qing Dynasty reached its apogee during the eighteenth century.

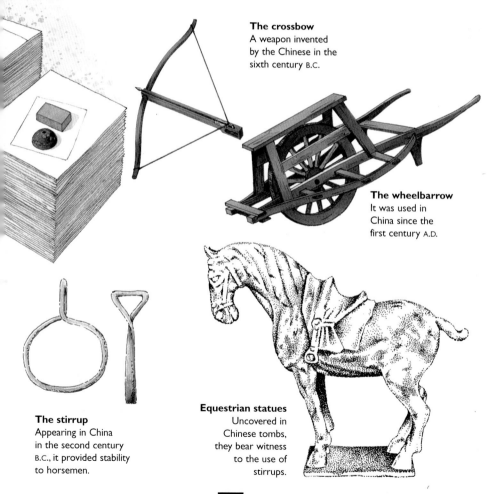

The crossbow
A weapon invented by the Chinese in the sixth century B.C.

The wheelbarrow
It was used in China since the first century A.D.

The stirrup
Appearing in China in the second century B.C., it provided stability to horsemen.

Equestrian statues
Uncovered in Chinese tombs, they bear witness to the use of stirrups.

The empire remained self-sufficient until the Western occupation at the beginning of the nineteenth century.

The military and the literati—the country's elite—maintained an attitude of disdain toward European science and culture and under-estimated the growing power of the Western nations.

Foreign commerce continued to hinge on the exportation of tea and silk in exchange for silver; every other European product was considered barbaric by the sophisticated ruling Chinese and Manchu classes.

Armor
In the Middle Ages it completely covered the horseman as well as the horse.

THE CAVALRY
Thanks to stirrups, from the eighth century on, horse and horseman became a single war machine. The horseman could arm himself with lance in rest and brandish cutting blows without losing his balance.

Europe restores itself

In the first half of the Middle Ages (between 500 and 1150) Europe found itself in a state of grave economic and cultural backwardness. Even potential conquerors, such as the Arabs, were not attracted to the idea of fighting to gain possession of cities in ruin, by now stripped of their riches.

And yet, starting in the eighth century, European society began to awaken from the technological lethargy into which it had fallen and entered a lengthy period of achievement starting in the eleventh century, the High Middle Ages.

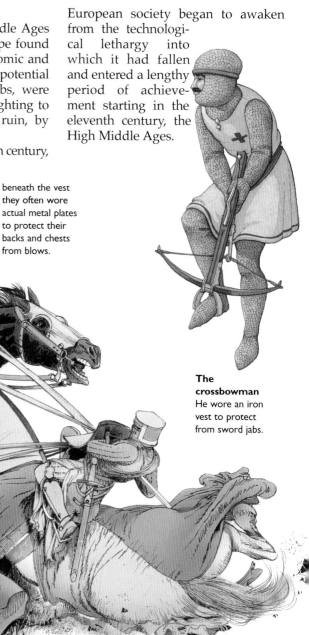

The cavalrymen
They had a sword, a lance, and a shield and were protected by iron helmets and vests. On top of or beneath the vest they often wore actual metal plates to protect their backs and chests from blows.

The crossbowman
He wore an iron vest to protect from sword jabs.

THE FORGE
Ironworking methods—largely ineffective—were passed down from the Greeks and Romans. To make a suit of armor it was necessary to burn down almost an entire forest for the furnace that smelted the metal.

The furnace
The iron material was heated with wood coals.

The bellows
Air was pumped to raise the temperature of the embers.

This turnabout was attributable to several factors, none of which was decisive in itself, but each of which certainly contributed to Europe's resurgence. One factor was increased attention to the classical world and contemporary Chinese and Arab civilizations. Europeans knew how to incorporate ideas and techniques of different cultures to their own advantage. Another factor was a state of necessity since they had neither slaves nor serfs for heavy work and they had to use their ingenuity to ease the hard work of farming the land. The political fragmentation of the Western world in the Middle Ages was much more capable of stimulating research for innovations and new ideas than of establishing a centralized power. The

Workmanship
Metal, while still red hot, was shaped by hammer strokes on the anvil.

The details
For refinement the metal object was placed over the fire and hammered again.

influence of the Christian religion put forth the vision of a rational and thinking God who had assigned humans the task of dominating and manipulating the world. The final factor was the state of war in which Europe found itself in the eighth century.

After Islamic expansion was stopped with the victory of Charles Martel at Tours in 732, the European continent was shaken by a series of civil wars and by a second wave of invasions by peoples originating from the north and east. This situation stimulated the development of increasingly powerful hurling weapons and more solid outfits of armor. The medieval suits of armor that still exist are proof of the remarkable ability of the smiths of the time.

The horse collar
It was padded and placed on the shoulders of the horse. The animal was at last able to exercise its full power.

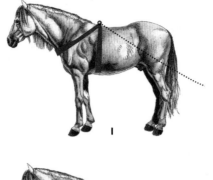

The harness
To haul carts, the Greeks and Romans placed a type of collar on their horses that pressed down on the jugular vein and the trachea (1). It has been calculated that with this method 80 percent of the animal's productivity was lost. The solution was found in the ninth century, with the conception of a belt that wound around the horse's shoulders instead of clenching its neck (2).

A further evolution
The definitive version of the horse's collar (3) appeared in the Late Middle Ages.

Improvements in ironworks were achieved above all thanks to northern blacksmiths. Those of Gaul, who in ages past had been praised by Caesar, invented mesh armor and iron treads for the wheels of carts. The Vikings' swords and the battle-axes of the Franks became renowned for their effectiveness.

But the real metallurgical innovation of the Middle Ages was that of cast iron. From the beginning of the Iron Age (from 1200 B.C.) until the late Middle Ages, iron material that was cast in furnaces never truly achieved the liquid state. With the gradual adoption of fossil coal as a combustible in place of wood coal and with increasingly powerful bellows, the temperature of the furnaces was raised.

In the fourteenth century, the construction of the first European blast furnaces, with their powerful airflow that increased the coal's combustion, made it possible to totally fuse the mineral. It was therefore possible to obtain cast iron, richer in carbon than traditional iron, which was less flexible but much more resistant to pressure.

The agricultural revolution

Metalworking had an enormous influence on agriculture. Among all of the metal instruments conceived to simplify the life of peasants, the heavy plow occupies a place of distinction. The spread of the heavy plow in northern Europe dates back to the seventh century and is the first in a series of

agricultural innovations that modified the face and role of Europe. Among the others are the use of water mills, triennial agrarian rotation, and new techniques in using horses, which progressively replaced oxen as draft animals. The number of oxen on an English abbey's farm was reduced by half between 1125 and 1160, and in the same period of time the number of draft horses quadrupled. This unexpected preference for the horse is explained by the diffusion of inventions that notably increase its efficiency.

The simple plow
Widespread throughout the Mediterranean area, it had an iron tip that dug shallow furrows that often necessitated two crisscrossed passings. It was ill-suited to the damp and heavy clay soils of the northern European plains.

The heavy plow
It dug deeply by using its two blades that cut through the soil both horizontally and vertically. It had wheels and a moldboard that overturned the cut clods of earth in such a way as to create deep furrows.

The most important invention was learning to shoe a horse: in ancient times the only means of protection for horses' hooves consisted of primitive leather sandals. Iron protected the horse's foot much better, especially on the wetlands of northern Europe. Another notable achievement was the improvement in harnessing. Comparable to the heavy plow for its influence on Europe's food production was the triennial rotation system that had begun in the eighth century. It was a solution for feeding the many draft animals that were necessary for plowing and to increase the harvests without completely depleting the land of its nutrients.

It was only during the Middle Ages that the water mill was employed in

The first year
Half of the field was designated for the cultivation of wheat and the other half for the farming of such things as barley and legumes.

CROP ROTATION
In the first half of the Middle Ages triennial rotation replaced the biennial one. This allowed for a fifty-percent increase in yield as well as for the production of food for horses used for farming, a determining factor in increasing agricultural yield still more.

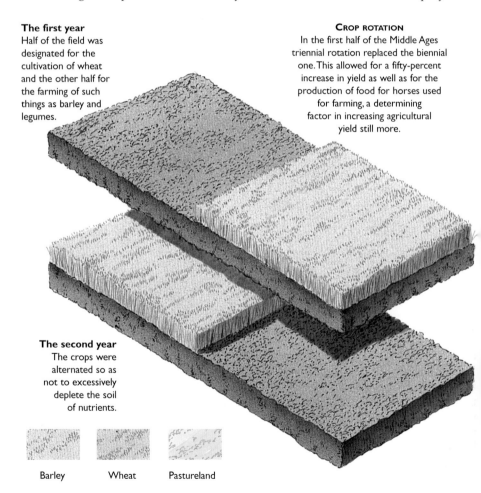

The second year
The crops were alternated so as not to excessively deplete the soil of nutrients.

Barley   Wheat   Pastureland

The first year
One-third of the land was sown in wheat.

The second year
Barley, oats, or legumes replaced the wheat, which was sown in what had been pasture the previous year.

The third year
After two years with different crops, each of the three fields was left unplanted, becoming pasture.

agriculture in a significant manner. Between the sixth and seventh centuries some feudal lords had water mills built, requiring their servants to use it for grinding wheat and prohibiting them from crushing the grain at home as they had always done. It proved very profitable and was quickly imitated by other landowners in every corner of Europe. Up until the tenth century, the water mill was only used to grind grain. It was also later utilized to convert the energy of flowing water into rotary motion to prepare malt for the production of beer, for ironworking, paper, and power saws in carpentry. This resulted in a gradual specialization of mills and millers.

In this same period the first windmills also appeared. The first recorded windmills were in Persia c. 650 and in common use in Europe c. 850. Their principal task was still that of grinding grain. The rapid proliferation of mills in Europe filled the void left by the chronic scarcity of labor available for work. Medieval Europe was probably the first society to base its economy on inanimate power rather than that of slaves, servants, or animals.

So many achievements in a relatively brief period of time had significant consequences. Later in the eleventh century, the end of the invasions brought a new tranquility to Europe. Fields could be farmed more easily, their yield increased, and the result was a greater availability of food. What followed was a great population increase and a political era called the Feudal Age. Large estates were controlled by a few landowners; their ruling style, permanent and inherited, favored a stronger and more effective exploitation of the land. By increasing cultivated areas, achieved by cutting down forest trees, the population quickly grew.

The rebirth of cities
The great agricultural revolution that changed the face of medieval fields immediately increased the production of food to accompany the growth of the European popula-

The horizontal wheel
The horizontal wheel transferred rotary motion to a vertical wheel by means of gears.

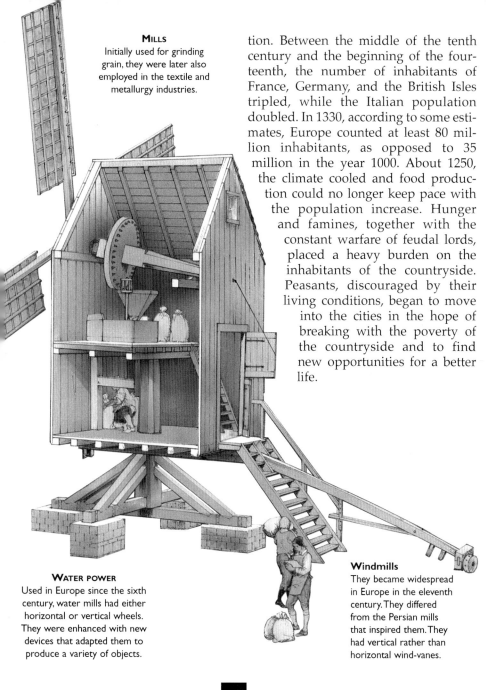

MILLS
Initially used for grinding grain, they were later also employed in the textile and metallurgy industries.

tion. Between the middle of the tenth century and the beginning of the fourteenth, the number of inhabitants of France, Germany, and the British Isles tripled, while the Italian population doubled. In 1330, according to some estimates, Europe counted at least 80 million inhabitants, as opposed to 35 million in the year 1000. About 1250, the climate cooled and food production could no longer keep pace with the population increase. Hunger and famines, together with the constant warfare of feudal lords, placed a heavy burden on the inhabitants of the countryside. Peasants, discouraged by their living conditions, began to move into the cities in the hope of breaking with the poverty of the countryside and to find new opportunities for a better life.

WATER POWER
Used in Europe since the sixth century, water mills had either horizontal or vertical wheels. They were enhanced with new devices that adapted them to produce a variety of objects.

Windmills
They became widespread in Europe in the eleventh century. They differed from the Persian mills that inspired them. They had vertical rather than horizontal wind-vanes.

GOTHIC CATHEDRALS
When viewed from within, these high buildings seemed to rest upon slender pillars, and in place of walls had very high windows. Beginning in the twelfth century, they made their first appearance in France.
The principle behind these structures was simple: free up internal space by supporting the structure from the outside.

The large windows
They were multi-colored and made of stained glass, which gave the cathedral a lighter image.

The flying buttress
It conveyed the force of the arch and the roof to the buttresses.

The Gothic arch
Given its similarity to the vertical arch, it directly released the weight to the underlying pillars.

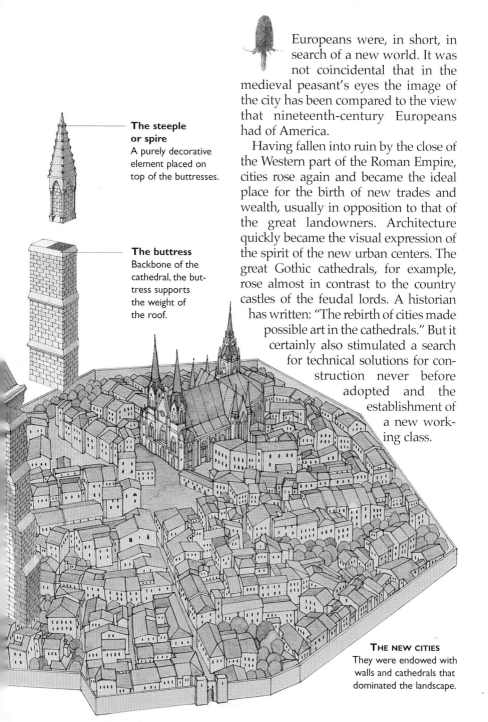

The steeple or spire
A purely decorative element placed on top of the buttresses.

The buttress
Backbone of the cathedral, the buttress supports the weight of the roof.

Europeans were, in short, in search of a new world. It was not coincidental that in the medieval peasant's eyes the image of the city has been compared to the view that nineteenth-century Europeans had of America.

Having fallen into ruin by the close of the Western part of the Roman Empire, cities rose again and became the ideal place for the birth of new trades and wealth, usually in opposition to that of the great landowners. Architecture quickly became the visual expression of the spirit of the new urban centers. The great Gothic cathedrals, for example, rose almost in contrast to the country castles of the feudal lords. A historian has written: "The rebirth of cities made possible art in the cathedrals." But it certainly also stimulated a search for technical solutions for construction never before adopted and the establishment of a new working class.

THE NEW CITIES
They were endowed with walls and cathedrals that dominated the landscape.

Actually, all of a city's artisans played a role in the construction of its cathedral: stonecutters, blacksmiths, carpenters, tinsmiths, and glassmakers.

The urban centers of ancient civilizations were always integrated with the farms, and power was held by landowners who lived predominantly in the city. The medieval city, on the other hand, quickly characterized itself as a self-contained entity, separated from the surrounding countryside, with its walls and moats. In the feudal world, exchanges took place in markets that occurred as infrequently as once a year. Cities, on the other hand, were theaters hosting a continuous interchange, populated by merchants and artisans who, organized into guilds, became increasingly richer and more powerful.

The state of relative well-being of the European citizens resulted in the production and consumption of goods previously considered superfluous, and also in the invention of new instruments.

New inventions

The mechanical weight clock made its appearance at the end of the thirteenth century. It is not known exactly who first conceived it, but European mechanics understood that the fall of a weight could be used to generate the regular oscillations necessary for the movement of a clock. Improvements were continual, so much so that after only one century every European city boasted its own clock, which not only announced the hour but also all the astronomical movements known at the time.

MERCHANDISE
Animals and utensils were purchased, as were luxury items such as mechanical clocks and Oriental fabrics.

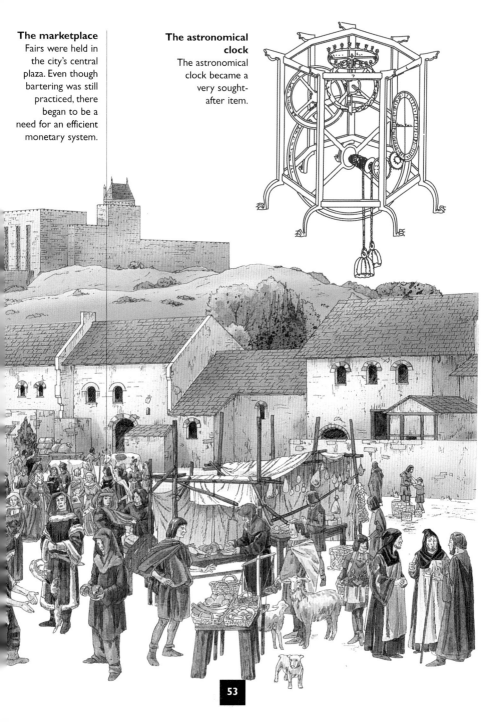

The marketplace
Fairs were held in the city's central plaza. Even though bartering was still practiced, there began to be a need for an efficient monetary system.

The astronomical clock
The astronomical clock became a very sought-after item.

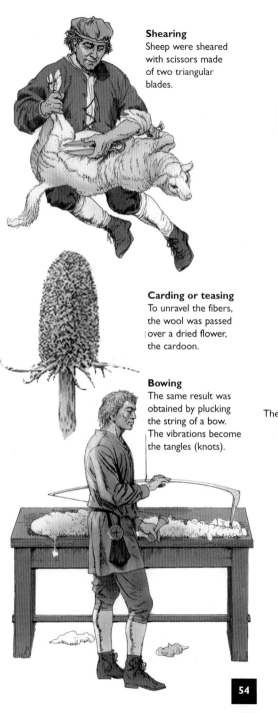

Shearing
Sheep were sheared with scissors made of two triangular blades.

Spinning
Women would twist the fiber and roll the yarn on a spindle.

Carding or teasing
To unravel the fibers, the wool was passed over a dried flower, the cardoon.

Bowing
The same result was obtained by plucking the string of a bow. The vibrations become the tangles (knots).

Milling
The thin-woven cloth made at the loom was pounded and pressed in water.

Weaving
In Europe, from the thirteenth century on, threads were woven on the horizontal treadle loom.

 Another area that underwent a strong increase in production was textiles. The production of fabric had always been a domestic occupation, but during the Middle Ages it developed into a series of specialized crafts such as that of weaver, fuller, dyer, and shearer. In Italy, the first industrial production systems appeared, and in some cases even men were employed, while in the past all textile activity was the exclusive domain of women. Technological innovations kept pace, with inventions such as the spinning wheel and a new version of the horizontal loom, which replaced the vertical one used since antiquity.

In short, the Europe that stood at the threshold of the sixteenth century was capable of producing goods and services as never before. But technology was surely the field that realized the greatest achievements. Fifteenth-century Europe could now consider itself equal to parts of the world that until that time were more advanced, such as the Islamic world and the Far East. Soon it quickly surpassed them.

The Renaissance

On May 29, 1453, the Turks conquered Constantinople, forcing many Greek scholars to flee to the West. Some historians often cite this date while others prefer 1492, the discovery of America, as the beginning of the Modern Age.

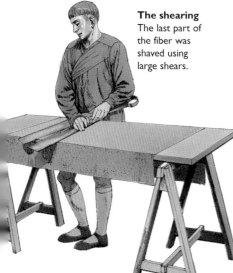

The shearing
The last part of the fiber was shaved using large shears.

It was this emigration of scholars from the Byzantine Empire that assisted Europe to rediscover classical culture, which had been cast into oblivion during the early Middle Ages. Rediscovering classical culture meant, indeed, the "rebirth" of its canons of beauty and harmony, its architectural genius, focusing attention on the heritage of texts and monuments of previous epochs and finding once again a concept of man as someone who changed the world and dominated nature. It was not by chance that scholars in this period were also known as Humanists.

This epoch is called the Renaissance and it influenced every field of knowl-

The structure
Completed in 1436, it consists of two domes that are superimposed, in brick. The internal diameter is 158 feet.

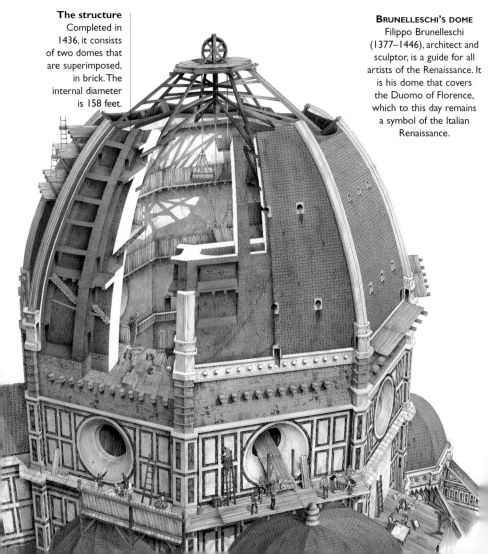

BRUNELLESCHI'S DOME
Filippo Brunelleschi (1377–1446), architect and sculptor, is a guide for all artists of the Renaissance. It is his dome that covers the Duomo of Florence, which to this day remains a symbol of the Italian Renaissance.

edge, from painting to sculpture, from architecture to philosophy: a virtual revolution of thought that would affect the fields of science and technology.

The Renaissance man is perfectly exemplified in the person of Leonardo da Vinci (1452–1519), a man capable of moving freely from painting to machine design to the study of human anatomy.

The entire European Renaissance was characterized by a flourishing of inventions not realized: steamships, calculators, and steam-powered wheels. If inventions were dated based on the year in which they were conceived, the Renaissance would have to be considered a period as creative as that of the Industrial Revolution, which began in 1750.

MACHINES
Conceived by Brunelleschi, they were studied by Leonardo da Vinci who in turn designed machines that in his age had no practical application. They would prove to be true technological prophecies if one considers the helicopter or the military tank.

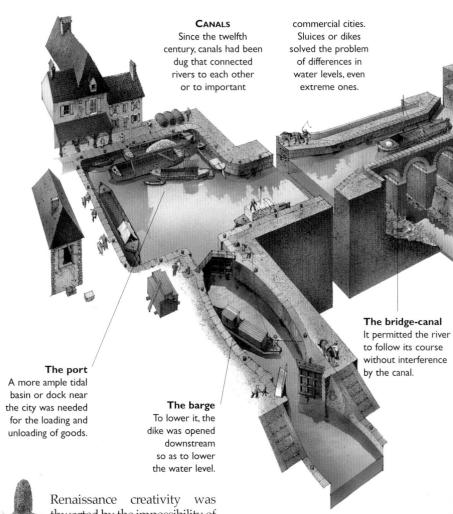

CANALS
Since the twelfth century, canals had been dug that connected rivers to each other or to important commercial cities. Sluices or dikes solved the problem of differences in water levels, even extreme ones.

The bridge-canal
It permitted the river to follow its course without interference by the canal.

The port
A more ample tidal basin or dock near the city was needed for the loading and unloading of goods.

The barge
To lower it, the dike was opened downstream so as to lower the water level.

Renaissance creativity was thwarted by the impossibility of performing certain jobs due to the lack of raw materials and sources of energy beyond that provided by animals. In spite of this, many ideas that did become realities contributed to the growth of the technological and economic gap between Europe and the rest of the world.

About 1497, Leonardo himself designed a system of sluices or dikes that made canal navigation much simpler. Hydraulic engineering was one of the major technological successes of the Renaissance.

In addition to Leonardo da Vinci, Dutch engineers also contributed to this

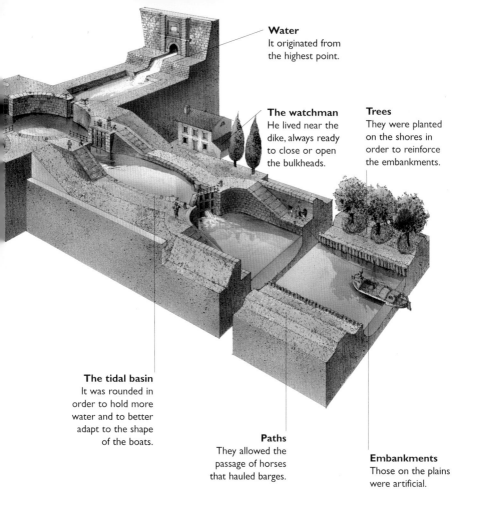

Water
It originated from the highest point.

The watchman
He lived near the dike, always ready to close or open the bulkheads.

Trees
They were planted on the shores in order to reinforce the embankments.

The tidal basin
It was rounded in order to hold more water and to better adapt to the shape of the boats.

Paths
They allowed the passage of horses that hauled barges.

Embankments
Those on the plains were artificial.

ield. They had to protect their land from the sea and from great rivers by building dikes, pumps, and canals. The great canal works also accelerated progress in the procurement of drinking water, an area in which Renaissance Europe still lagged behind the Romans.

Printing

A technological innovation of incal-culable importance was that of printing. In actuality the printing of characters and drawings by means of blocks of wood that were first etched and then dyed with ink was an ancient custom used on textiles in India c. 200 B.C., and spread quickly to China and the Middle East. The Chinese began printing on paper c. 500. By the 1400s block printing was common in Europe.

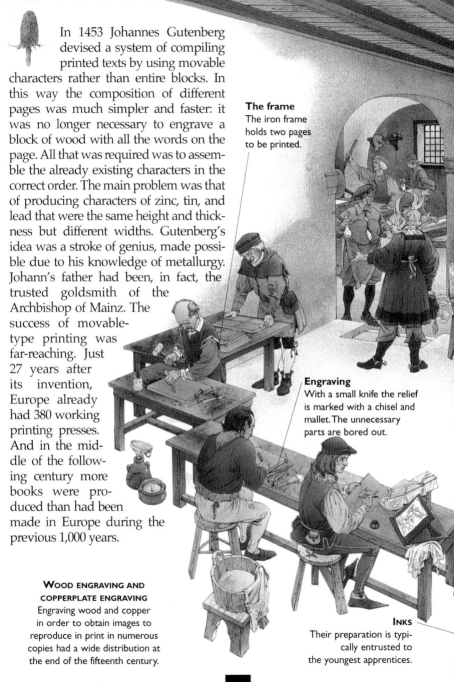

In 1453 Johannes Gutenberg devised a system of compiling printed texts by using movable characters rather than entire blocks. In this way the composition of different pages was much simpler and faster: it was no longer necessary to engrave a block of wood with all the words on the page. All that was required was to assemble the already existing characters in the correct order. The main problem was that of producing characters of zinc, tin, and lead that were the same height and thickness but different widths. Gutenberg's idea was a stroke of genius, made possible due to his knowledge of metallurgy. Johann's father had been, in fact, the trusted goldsmith of the Archbishop of Mainz. The success of movable-type printing was far-reaching. Just 27 years after its invention, Europe already had 380 working printing presses. And in the middle of the following century more books were produced than had been made in Europe during the previous 1,000 years.

The frame
The iron frame holds two pages to be printed.

Engraving
With a small knife the relief is marked with a chisel and mallet. The unnecessary parts are bored out.

WOOD ENGRAVING AND COPPERPLATE ENGRAVING
Engraving wood and copper in order to obtain images to reproduce in print in numerous copies had a wide distribution at the end of the fifteenth century.

INKS
Their preparation is typically entrusted to the youngest apprentices.

TYPESETTING
A typographer organizes the characters on the page; another measures the line to be printed with a composing stick.

SPREADING THE INK
It is achieved by passing pads along the background of the page.

THE PRESS
A sheet is pressed on a form upon which the inked movable characters are fixed. In this way the printed page is born.

THE SHEETS OF PAPER
The printed proofs are checked by a reader.

The flintlock
Pulling the trigger of the gun caused a flint to ignite a spark that sets the powders on fire.

Firearms
At the beginning of the fifteenth century pieces of artillery made of hammered iron were commonly used during sieges.

Cannons

Before metalsmiths succeeded in producing barrels that were resistant and perfectly hollowed, they devised cannons anchored to a wooden framework.

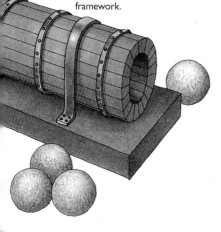

Gunpowder

It is effectively stored in a horn. Its use radically changed the method of combat. But it also changed the way ships and fortresses were built.

The immediate result was the lowering of the price of books, before then considered a luxury that few were able to afford. Gutenberg's invention ushered in a new era, one permitting a rapid and widespread diffusion of ideas and knowledge throughout Europe.

Firearms

Another sector in which the supremacy of Europe was affirmed during the Renaissance was that of firearms. The terms harquebus, flintlock, and musket were coined between the fifteenth and sixteenth centuries, when there was a notable improvement in the manufacture of portable firearms. This occurred not so much to meet military needs, but because hunting was becoming more and more popular as a recreational activity. Indeed, the hunting rifles had to be comfortable to shoulder and precise in their aim, whereas in battle precision was of little importance. It was enough to fire at a group of amassed troops in close formations. The one true technical difficulty was that of producing a barrel that was perfectly smooth inside or, better yet, uniformly rifled. Only in 1525 was this last improvement, whose advantages in terms of the bullet's trajectory were already known in the Middle Ages, put into practice. Cannons became ever more powerful and precise, resulting in a radical change in battle techniques and strategies on both land and sea.

An important innovation was the ability to load the cannon from its posterior side rather than from its mouth. It was thus no longer necessary to pull back cannons on ships before being able to use them again. Even the Chinese, the inventors of firearms, were greatly surprised when in 1514 they saw their seas lined with Portuguese sailing vessels armed with revolving cannons.

Navigation

During the 1400s ocean-going ships were developed, combining the best of the Mediterranean maritime tradition with the Nordic one. They were equipped with three masts with both

The caravel
With its three masts and its pressure hull, it permitted ocean navigation. It was at the command of three caravels that Christopher Columbus completed the voyage that on October 12, 1492 would lead him to America.

The compass
It was first used in the 11th century by the Chinese but was perfected in the 12th century

square Nordic sails and Latin triangular sails. The sail became more efficient in taking advantage of wind power. To locate their position in the immense expanses of ocean waters, navigators also had to equip themselves with new instruments and information. In the fourteenth century the astrolabe and the quadrant were introduced to measure altitude. Europe's oceanic expansion changed the course of history. A greater transportation capacity and the speed of the new ships had immediate economic consequences. But European fleets were also employed to explore and conquer territories that until then had been unknown.

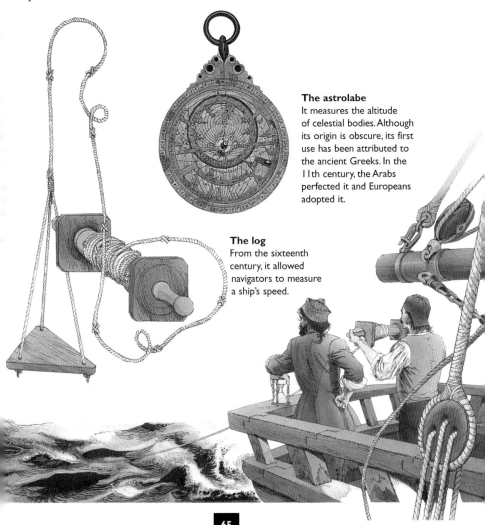

The astrolabe
It measures the altitude of celestial bodies. Although its origin is obscure, its first use has been attributed to the ancient Greeks. In the 11th century, the Arabs perfected it and Europeans adopted it.

The log
From the sixteenth century, it allowed navigators to measure a ship's speed.

The birth of science

The Renaissance was the period in which Europeans achieved world importance, based, in part, upon Europe's supremacy in technology. But between the fifteenth and eighteenth centuries Europe also distinguished itself for its great acceleration in culture. Perhaps the most important event of the epoch was the birth of modern science with its many and varied technological applications. Until the late Middle Ages the study of natural phenomena and their practical application remained two completely distinct endeavors. It was only in the 1600s that it became evident that a knowledge of nature could lead to the ability of controlling its forces and consequently the possibility of producing machines to exploit them.

Behind the revolution was the English philosopher Francis Bacon (1561–1626), the Italian scientist Galileo Galilei (1564–1642), the French philosopher René Descartes (1596–1650), and the English scientist Isaac Newton (1642–1727). The advances during this time signaled the intellectual emancipation from the ancient world. For centuries the authority of the Greek philosopher Aristotle (384–322 B.C.) in physics, of Ptolemy (A.D. 138–178) in geography and astronomy, and of Galen (A.D. 129–201) in medicine had been absolute. With the introduction of the scientific method by Galileo, the validity of a scientific theory would now be based solely on observation of results and on repeated experimentation.

The scientific revolution did not, however, have immediate technological repercussions. Only a few techniques,

THE EXPERIMENT
An inclined plane allows Galileo Galilei to calculate the velocity of falling bodies and to formulate his laws of motion.

**Isaac Newton
(1642–1727)**
He discovered the law of gravity that governs the movement of the planets.

**Galileo Galilei
(1564–1642)**
He is considered the father of the scientific method.

66

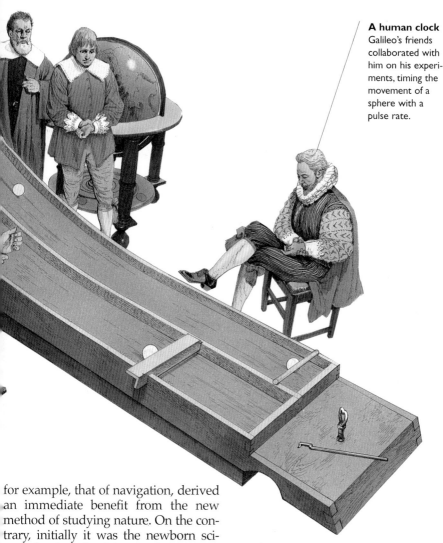

A human clock
Galileo's friends collaborated with him on his experiments, timing the movement of a sphere with a pulse rate.

for example, that of navigation, derived an immediate benefit from the new method of studying nature. On the contrary, initially it was the newborn science that benefited from technology. In fact, some crucial results were obtained thanks only to precision instruments built for this purpose. The discovery of the moons of Jupiter, for instance, would not have occurred had Galileo not built his telescope. In spite of the great discoveries of pure science, the technology of the sixteenth and seventeenth centuries did not significantly diverge from that of preceding eras. New information penetrated European society slowly, but it paved the way for an event that would increase its supremacy over the rest of the world in future centuries: the Industrial Revolution.

THE INDUSTRIAL REVOLUTION

In the 1700s, in England, the accumulation of wealth and the application of science to technology gave rise to a series of industrial developments that would first bring Europe, and then other parts of the world, to an unprecedented level of prosperity.

European technology had made giant leaps during the Middle Ages and the Renaissance. In spite of this, during the first half of the 1700s Europe's economy was based exclusively on agriculture and trade. But from 1750, and for the next one hundred years, an evolution of techniques occurred that was so vast it profoundly affected all aspects of civilization and transformed the European economy into one based on industry and manufacturing. European men and women went from being shepherds-farmers-artisans to being operators of machines powered by inanimate energy. The Industrial Revolution began in England in the eighteenth century and from there spread slowly to other countries on the European continent. Exactly why did

The miner's friend
It was a kettle that converted water into steam. By cooling it quickly, the steam condensed. This operation created a vacuum, which could then suction underground water.

Watt's machine
With the cylinder displacement, it was twice as powerful as its predecessors.

The steam engine
It is the symbol of the Industrial Revolution: for the first time it placed great amounts of energy at man's disposal.

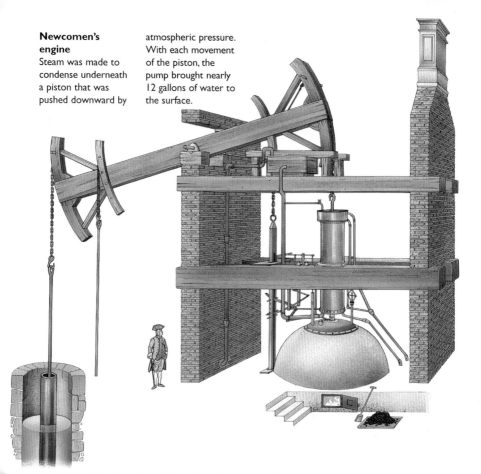

Newcomen's engine
Steam was made to condense underneath a piston that was pushed downward by atmospheric pressure. With each movement of the piston, the pump brought nearly 12 gallons of water to the surface.

it begin in England and at that time? Economic historians have suggested various factors.

The first was the profitability of agriculture, enhanced by legal and technical advances, increased entrepreneurial investments in this field as well as in the manufacturing sector with its rising factories; 2) the availability of cheap labor; 3) the establishment of England as a world power and the wealth it derived from this status; 4) the fact that England represented a relatively unified market in which people and goods could circulate easily, thereby stimulating demand and supply; 5) legislation that tended to protect the rights and profits of inventors; and 6) the availability of coal, the fuel of the Industrial Revolution, and the ease with which it could be transported from its extraction sites thanks to many navigable waterways: in short, a series of reasons that very early on created a wide gap between England and the rest of Europe.

In terms of technological innovations, industrialization influenced three sectors: animal and human labor was replaced by inanimate power thanks to the steam engine and the methods of extraction, as well as the manipulation, of raw materials improved. In the end many jobs that had previously been entrusted to people were performed by machines.

The steam engine

As stated at the end of the previous chapter, between 1600 and 1700 science had assumed an increasingly important role in European society. The study and understanding of natural phenomena were no longer the exclusive pre-

Jacquard's mechanical loom

Its invention was a very important step in the automation of the textile industry. The design of the fabric was programmed on punch cards that controlled the machine's work. In only 11 years, between 1800 and 1811, France boasted 11,000 machines of this type, which required only one operator to make them run.

THE MINES
Extracting metals and especially coal from beneath the ground was crucial to industrial development. Children were employed to transport the wagons, an extremely exhausting task.

rogative of philosophers, but began to be part of the cultural challenge toward invention. A prime example was the steam engine. The first step in its execution was the discovery of the existence of atmospheric pressure by the Italian scientist Evangelista Torricelli (1608–1647) who invented the barometer in 1643.

The problem at first was an extremely practical one: the technicians of the Grand Duke of Tuscany were unsuccessful in raising water that was about 15 yards below ground with a suction pump. Torricelli understood that the solution to this problem rested in the layer of air that hangs over the earth, a force capable of causing mercury to rise in a tube 30 inches high. Torricelli's discovery launched a series of experiments on the properties of atmospheric pressure and vacuum.

The first real steam engine was constructed in 1698 by the English engineer Thomas Savery and was used to raise water that had become stagnant in mines; for this reason it was called "the miner's friend." In the same period Thomas Newcomen designed a machine that, while based on the same principles, was safer and more practical.

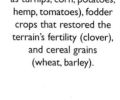 Achievements in improving engines were continual and in some cases decisive for the future of this invention.

. The invention of the most efficient steam engine is linked to the name of the Scotsman James Watt (1736–1819), who, with a series of devices, more than quadrupled its output.

The diffusion of engines

Watt's engine finally made possible the conversion of coal's chemical energy into mechanical energy: for this reason, the presence of easily accessible coal deposits was of decisive importance to England's industrial development.

The Industrial Revolution triggered a virtual cycle of invention and production. The use of the steam engine was responsible for an increase in the production of fuel, as it furnished inanimate energy at low cost and facilitated the extraction of minerals (especially coal), therefore contributing to the growth of the mining and metallurgy industries.

But all fields of production benefitted from the introduction of new machines that increased productivity and reduced the workload of laborers. In the textile industry, for example, achievements were astounding. From prehistoric times it had been the fingers of women that transformed the shapeless skeins of wool into yarn. People had to wait until 1738 for someone to suggest that the same result could be obtained with two thread rolls.

THE NORFOLK ROTATION
It was the rotation, on the same plot of land, in a four-year cycle, of renewable crops (such as turnips, corn, potatoes, hemp, tomatoes), fodder crops that restored the terrain's fertility (clover), and cereal grains (wheat, barley).

Turnips

Wheat

Barley

Clover

In 1801 the first robots made their appearance in textile mills when the loom set up by the Frenchman Joseph Marie Jacquard began to function in a way that is similar to modern computers. The information concerning the design of the fabric was stored on punch cards (perforated cards), and the loom thus proceeded automatically without the intervention of operators.

The increase in industrial production was not as immediate or spectacular as could be imagined; it became so only after 1820. Nonetheless, it gave rise to a notable increase in the population. Europe's population (excluding Russia) went from 120 million people in 1750 to 210 million in 1850. To feed all of these new Europeans, agriculture was forced to produce more. During the second half of the eighteenth century in Great Britain, the four-year cycle of crops, known as the Norfolk Rotation, became widespread. This ultimately resulted in an increase in the yield of fields that had been producing generous outputs for decades. From original stores of food came the money for investment in industry. Between the end of the 1700s and the beginning of the 1800s, several mechanical devices appeared that would till the soil, sow, reap, and thresh.

A passion for machines of every kind was certainly one of the characteristics of the Industrial Revolution. Leonardo da Vinci, who had conceived and designed complex machines, comes to mind from ages past.

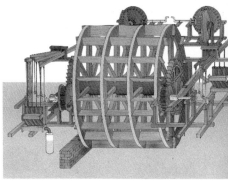

The waterwheel
It converted water current into mechanical energy. It also served to replenish drinkable water in cities.

The dulcimer player
It is a 1785 device that held a toothed cylinder gear and cams, the two devices that control the motion.

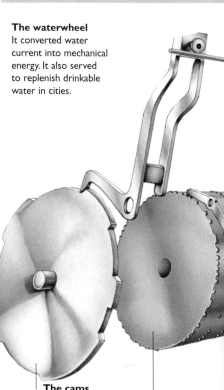

In spite of the steam engine's success, Great Britain's principal source of energy was supplied by river currents. Entire generations of engineers dedicated themselves, with their gigantic wheels, to squeezing energy from every moving drop of water.

Some of their colleagues, on the other hand, devoted themselves to designing machine tools, crucial to the development of an industrial economy. The tools designed for the various kinds of workmanship, even those

The cams
Irregularly shaped disks set the arm in motion, toward the left and toward the right.

The toothed cylinder gear
It activated the mechanism for the fingers.

used by artisans, actually consisted of devices whose application could also be useful in several different areas including factories.

Until 1780, tools were more or less the same as those used by medieval artisans; by 1850, all modern machine tools, from the lathe to the automatic planer, had been invented. The industrial lathe was invented by the Eng-lishman Henry Maudslay and the milling machine was invented by the American Eli Whitney in the early 1800s. But mechanisms and machines were also the protagonists of a virtual fashion rage. Mechanical dolls and automated musical instruments were exhibited in the salons of the nobility and the upper middle class, a style in step with the spirit of the age.

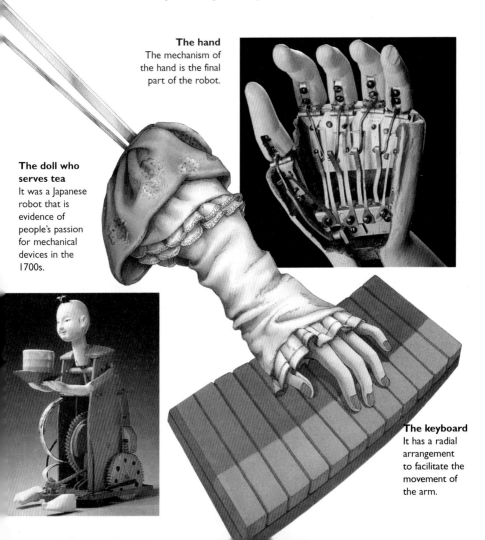

The hand
The mechanism of the hand is the final part of the robot.

The doll who serves tea
It was a Japanese robot that is evidence of people's passion for mechanical devices in the 1700s.

The keyboard
It has a radial arrangement to facilitate the movement of the arm.

Philosophers such as Déscartes hypothesized that living beings were comparable to particularly sophisticated mechanical devices.

The Royal Society and the *Encyclopédie*

The mechanistic conception of the world was reinforced by the birth of institutions whose goal was the advancement of science and the spread of scientific culture throughout society. The Royal Society, the first European scientific society, was founded in London in 1660: it contributed to the birth of a technological culture based on scientific knowledge more than on experience accumulated by generations of artisans. It brought together a new society of men interested in physics and its applications and stimulated the publication of scientific and technical discoveries, thus making them known to everyone. With the passage of time the propagation of scientific knowledge and its applications assumed a philanthropic value. Benjamin Thompson, Count Rumford, for example, in 1796 proposed the establishment of an assistance house for the poor that was affiliated with an institution capable of producing and propagating new inventions.

During the years of the French Revolution the conviction that science and technology were capable of liberating people from heavy labor became more widespread. The famous *Encyclopédie* compiled by Denis Diderot and Jean D'Alembert was marked by a rationalism typical of the Age of Enlightenment, and, thanks to its breadth,

The Royal Society It organized explorations to every corner of the world. The exploration of the Pacific Ocean, led by James Cook in 1768, is a famous one.

Diderot and D'Alembert
They codified all the scientific and technological knowledge of the epoch in their *Encyclopédie*, published in 39 volumes between 1751 and 1772.

organized the science and technology of the time.

But science and technology also became definitive fields of study. Indeed, special schools were founded for future mathematicians and engineers. The most celebrated example is Paris's Polytechnical School, founded in 1794.

By now inventions could no longer be attributed to a stroke of genius or good fortune, but to the study of natural phenomena. The Industrial Revolution had sanctioned the marriage of science and technology, a union that would blossom during the second half of the nineteenth century.

THE AGE OF OPTIMISM

The telephone, electric lighting, the train, and the automobile all appeared in the second half of the nineteenth century and changed the way of life of Europeans and Americans: it was the second Industrial Revolution, an era that seemed limitless in its potential for technological progress.

In 1851 London hosted a great international exhibition where the new inventions of the world were presented. No other event better represented the great optimism that the explosion of science and technology gave rise to in Europe. Visiting the exhibition, all social classes understood the possibilities of the infant industrial era. Even Queen Victoria marveled at the technological successes achieved by her subjects and congratulated herself and her husband, who was one of the exhibition's organizers. After having visited the exhibition she wrote in her diary: "God bless my dear Albert and my dear nation, that today have demonstrated their greatness." But what was so exhilarating about the London exhibition of 1851? From accounts of the time, we learn that the major achievements of the Industrial Revolution

Telephone networks
The first ones appeared in Great Britain's large cities in the second half of the nineteenth century. The first telephones had two components: one for speaking and one for listening. An operator connected the various customers.

were presented on that occasion: from machine tools to reapers, from pendulum clocks to sewing machines.

In the middle of the nineteenth century any European citizen who was familiar with the achievements of technology could not help but imagine a future made up of continual advances, with machines that would facilitate any type of work and render even simple everyday activities easier to perform. Around 1850 technological innovation underwent a further acceleration involving France, Prussia, and above all, the United States.

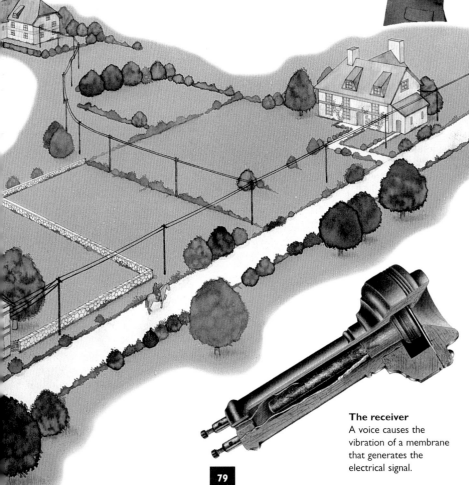

The receiver
A voice causes the vibration of a membrane that generates the electrical signal.

After 1850 science and scientists became increasingly important in terms of technological change, to the point that they almost took over its direction. The exploitation of hydraulic energy and chemical energy, for example, depended in a critical way on scientific achievements. Instruction played a fundamental role. In the second half of the nineteenth century the level of technological advancement of every nation depended upon the number of scientists and technicians at their disposal and upon the average level of education of its population. This combination of phenomena, for the impetus it generated and the transformations it provoked within society, has been compared to the era of the English Industrial Revolution of the 1700s. For this very reason, the period it shaped has been defined by scholars as the era of the Second Industrial Revolution.

While the 1700s were years of the mechanization of the textile industry, steam engines, and cast iron, the last 20 years of the 1800s were instead characterized by steel and chemistry, by oil

SANITATION SERVICES
During the course of the 1800s, a few European cities such as London were supplied with sewer systems that collected the sewage of single apartments and led the flow into large subterranean mains.

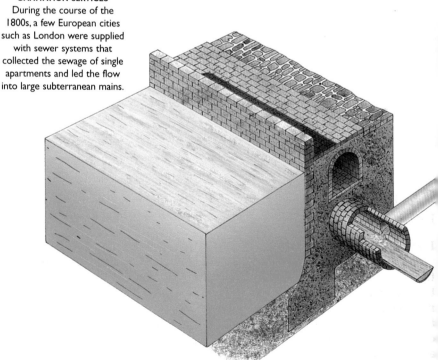

The indoor bathroom
It was invented in 1778 by the Englishman Joseph Bramah. The sewage was often collected beside the buildings in large ditches that were emptied daily.

Running water
The improvement of hygienic conditions was also due to the increased use of running water in homes and to continually improved sinks and bathtubs, first in metal, then, about the end of the 1800s, in ceramic.

and electricity, and by technology placed in the service of daily life.

Electricity

At the beginning of the 1800s, electricity was nothing more than a scientific curiosity. Thanks, as always, to research and experiments, it became a form of energy used first in communications, a little later in the metallurgy and chemical industries, and finally in public lighting.

The primary discoveries were made by scientists of different nationalities. Most memorable were the American Benjamin Franklin, the Italian Alessandro Volta, and the British inventor Michael Faraday, the first to understand, in 1831, that there was a connection between magnetic fields and electric currents.

Faraday's insight, together with the progress of steam engines, paved the way for the construction of mechanical generators of electricity that were based on the principle of the workings of a modern-day bicycle.

The discovery of electric current had the greatest impact on the communications sector. In 1837 both Samuel F. B. Morse in the United States and two English inventors, William Cooke and Charles Wheatstone, patented a telegraph that allowed communication between train stations. But the telegraph, which eventually was extremely successful, only transmitted sequence of beeps. Much more practical was an instrument that could transmit word electrically. The first attempts to produce a telephone date back to 1861, when Philipp Reis displayed one, little more than a toy, at Frankfurt on the Main.

The cinématographe of the brothers Lumière
The first short film was presented in France on February 13, 1895.

THE FIRST PROJECTION
On December 28, 1895, 33 people had the privilege of attending the first cinematographic projection in history, *The Arrival of the Train at the Station.* One week later the spectators numbered more than 2,000.

What would become one of the most widely used means of communication in the world was instead patented by Alexander Graham Bell in 1876, in spite of a dispute over the paternity of the idea with the Italian Antonio Meucci. This dispute was resolved in favor of Bell by a ruling of the Supreme Court of the United States. The telephone's success was almost immedi- ate: in 1878 the first commercial receiver was introduced in England, and the following year the first telephone exchange that permitted calls to be put through between many different users was installed in London.

Daily Life

Since ancient times all technological efforts had been aimed at meeting the

Lighting
Gas lighting spread throughout major cities. It was slowly replaced by electric lighting.

basic needs of communities of human beings: defending themselves against enemies, obtaining the greatest amount of food with the least amount of work, building dwellings that would protect them from the outside world. But from the middle of the nineteenth century on, many Europeans found these primary needs met. It was because of this that inventors and scientists began to concentrate on making life in the cities safer and more pleasant.

Much progress was made in the area of public hygiene, but the cities of the industrialized world, besides being cleaner, also became less dark during the night: gas lamps, invented in 1799 by the French engineer Philippe Lebon, spread rapidly and would be used until the beginning of the twentieth century.

The nineteenth century was also the century of electric lighting. The crucial invention was Thomas Alva Edison's incandescent light (1880). Edison opened the first power plants in London and New York in 1882. The advent of public lighting, however, gave rise to a demand that could only be met by a centralized system of energy generation and distribution. Europe's first public power plant was built at Godalming, England, by the brothers Siemens in 1881. In the next 15 years, others sprang up throughout Western Europe and the United States, each with its own facilities and transmission methods.

New forms of entertainment and artistic expression were born. In 1839, Louis Daguerre demonstrated the first photograph in France. When it

Locomotives
Between 1850 and 1870, 50,000 miles of new railroad tracks were built in Europe (compared to 15,000 in all the preceding years).

Emigration
Millions of Europeans saw the steamship as a means of escaping poverty. America was a place of opportunities.

became known that photography had been invented, the painter Paul Delaroche exclaimed, "From this day on painting is dead!" His prediction was mistaken, but certainly the faithful reproduction of images on plates or film had far-reaching and numerous applications, in science as well as in art and commerce.

The same is true for the movie industry, born at the end of the 1800s. The first moving object was photographed repeatedly on the same plate in 1874, and the first film was projected in public in 1895. Thomas Edison developed the first kinetoscope, the forerunner of motion pictures. He also patented the first successful phonograph in 1878.

THE GREAT SHIPS
They increased the importation of raw materials. For example, between 1840 and 1870, Great Britain increased its importation of wool 200-fold.

Power
In 1807, American Robert Fulton built the first commercially successful steamboat. In 1893, a steamship could discharge a power equal to 60,000 horsepower. In 1829, the first steamship discharged only 60.

1   **2**   **3**   **4**

KARL BENZ

His motorized three-wheeler was presented to the public on July 3, 1886. Its commercial success was such that, in 1901, hundreds of models were sold.

The three-wheeler

It could reach a maximum speed of 13 kilometers per hour.

The gas motor
It has a four-phased operating cycle
1) Expansion:
The piston descends toward the bottom and sucks up the gasoline that enters the cylinder.
2) Compression:
The valves close and the piston rises toward the top.

3) Combustion:
The spark ignites the mixture of fuel and pushes the piston down.
4) Exhaust:
The valves open: The piston rises again and expels the remnants of the combustion.

Distances narrow

The most revolutionary technological innovations of the nineteenth century involved the transportation of persons, goods, raw materials, and energy. The steam engine played a central role.

In transportation over water, the sail gave way to the steam engine in 1838, the year in which it proved capable of transatlantic service. Until 1890 sailboats dominated the seas, but steam engines made remarkable achievements in the area of power supply. The immediate result was increased importation of raw materials from far away places and the movement of large numbers of people all over the Earth.

Toward the end of the century the train was already the most widely used mode of transportation. By linking the inlands to principal ports the railway network allowed European food supplies to increase and diversify.

The end of the nineteenth century saw the birth of the automobile. The first models resembled a locomotive more than a modern motor vehicle: they did not have a gas motor but instead used a boiler and ran on the force of steam power. French engineer Etienne Lenoir invented the first successful internal combustion engine in 1860 and installed it in a crude automobile. It was immediately clear that the vehicle of the future would not ultimately be powered by steam. The German Rudolf Diesel patented the first internal combustion engine to use low-grade fuel oil in 1892. The predecessor of the modern automobile was made by the German Karl Benz, who in 1885 constructed a light three-wheeled vehicle powered by a gas motor. In 1893 he added a fourth wheel, and this model had a notable commercial success.

Another German inventor, Gottlieb Daimler, introduced some essential modifications to the combustion engine and also produced successful automobiles. In the United States, Henry Ford had worked for six years on the idea of a horseless carriage. In 1896 he built and tested his first automobile, one that reached a speed of 48 miles per hour.

In 1900, only a few years after the first reliable models were introduced, there were 9,000 automobiles in circulation in Europe and less than 5,000 in the United States. By 1916, in the United States, this number rose to 1 1/2 million.

The age of iron and steel

Iron and steel were two crucial elements in the technological explosion that started in 1850. Steamships that had iron and later steel hulls, or the web of train tracks that wound around Europe are examples. But it was in architecture that iron and steel were used in the most spectacular and innovative way, often built for the sole purpose of demonstrating their amazing dimensions and imposing structure. The Eiffel Tower, erected in Paris for the occasion of the exhibition of 1889, was built using 7,300 tons of iron and measured 984 feet. Even the London exhibition of 1851 had had a building in which great use of iron had been made. The organizers of the exhibition needed a grandiose construc-

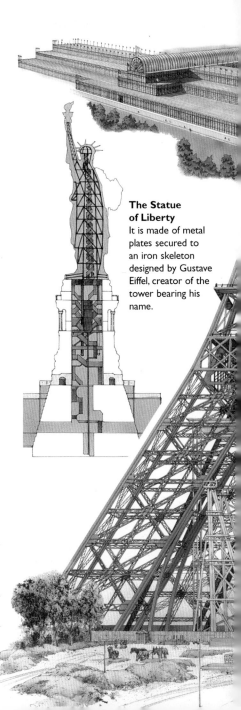

The Statue of Liberty
It is made of metal plates secured to an iron skeleton designed by Gustave Eiffel, creator of the tower bearing his name.

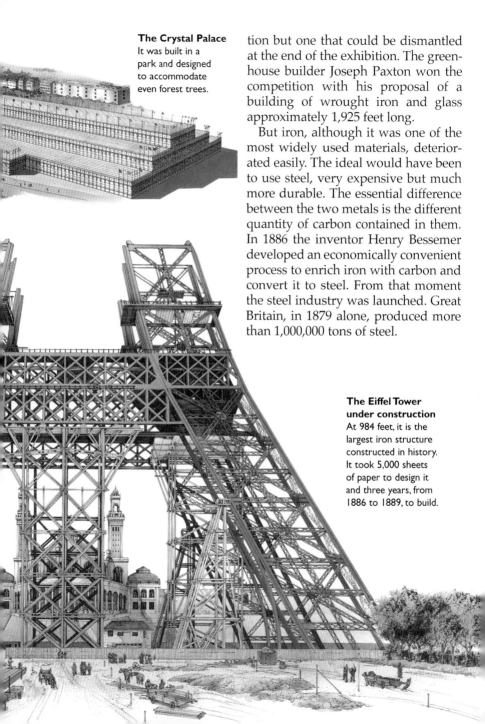

The Crystal Palace
It was built in a park and designed to accommodate even forest trees.

tion but one that could be dismantled at the end of the exhibition. The greenhouse builder Joseph Paxton won the competition with his proposal of a building of wrought iron and glass approximately 1,925 feet long.

But iron, although it was one of the most widely used materials, deteriorated easily. The ideal would have been to use steel, very expensive but much more durable. The essential difference between the two metals is the different quantity of carbon contained in them. In 1886 the inventor Henry Bessemer developed an economically convenient process to enrich iron with carbon and convert it to steel. From that moment the steel industry was launched. Great Britain, in 1879 alone, produced more than 1,000,000 tons of steel.

The Eiffel Tower under construction
At 984 feet, it is the largest iron structure constructed in history. It took 5,000 sheets of paper to design it and three years, from 1886 to 1889, to build.

The new machines

Among the great successes of nineteenth-century technology are a series of machines of greater or lesser complexity. Some, employed in basic sectors such as agriculture, had an immediate impact on life and production activities. The mechanical reaper of Cyrus McCormick, for example, was invented in 1831 and immediately used on most farms of the United States. And in 1837, John Deere, another American, developed a self-cleaning steel plow that allowed for more efficient, deeper plowing.

Agricultural machines did not achieve immediate success due to the lack of available energy sources. While factories availed themselves of steam engines to power their machinery, the combine harvesters still had to be hauled by horses. Still, albeit slowly, new steel implements, steam threshers, mechanical sowers, and reapers spread throughout farms, increasing production.

Another machine invented during the 1800s was the sewing machine

Charles Babbage (1792–1871)
His mechanical calculator contained 5,000 gears.

The Reaper
Two rows of short triangular knives, placed in the front part of the machine, move reciprocally to chop down the wheat.

There were many attempts to reproduce the movement of the sewing hand mechanically. During the first half of the century virtually 17 different sewing machines were invented, but none of them worked well. The American Isaac Merrit Singer perfected one and put into production models that were operated by pressing a pedal.

Its success was astounding: Singer produced 2,200 sewing machines in 853, 500,000 in 1870.

In those same years the typewriter was also patented. An American company, Remington, acquired the patent in 1874 and made way for the production of this new instrument that would radically change the job of office workers.

Calculators were also designed, without much success, during this period. This was the case with Charles Babbage, an English mathematician who invested his entire fortune to make a mechanical predecessor of modern computers.

THE CENTURY OF SCIENCE

Science and technology no longer depended upon the ingenuity of the inventor, but rather on research funded by countries and private companies. The new physics has changed people's perception of their world. The applications of science can result either in increased well-being or catastrophe.

The twentieth century announced its scientific predilection early on. The radio and the first flight of a motorized airplane were only the first novelties of the century. Science predominated the new age. In a short time scientists presented an impressive series of discoveries. Some were achieved by experimentation; others by theoretical process. Thus was born the science of theoretical physics of which Albert Einstein was the principal exponent. In 1905 the young scientist introduced the special theory of relativity, and in 1916, the general theory of relativity. He became the symbol of the twentieth century, influencing knowledge, and contributing to the profound modification of people's view of science and of the world.

The twentieth century saw the birth of quantum mechanics, a theory that unveiled the secrets of the atom and its

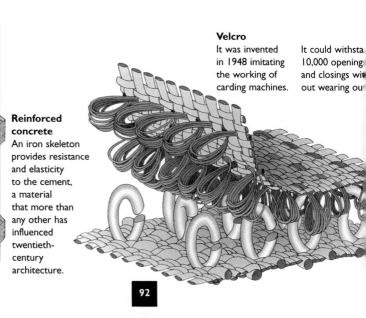

Velcro
It was invented in 1948 imitating the working of carding machines. It could withsta 10,000 opening and closings wit out wearing ou

Reinforced concrete
An iron skeleton provides resistance and elasticity to the cement, a material that more than any other has influenced twentieth-century architecture.

components. Besides all the great theories, many scientific discoveries took place as well. The technological revolution, of which we reap the benefits today, is due to these.

Used for progress but also capable of being used for the destruction of humanity, science and technology proceed more and more on an equal footing: the new scenario is *big science,* that is, the combining of efforts and talents of the large number of scientists and technicians organized by the ambitious programs of world powers.

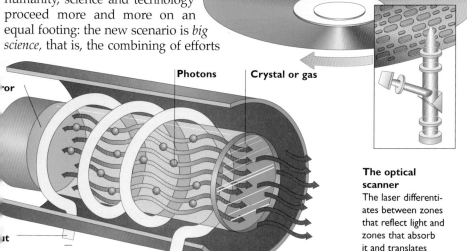

Photons | Crystal or gas

The optical scanner
The laser differentiates between zones that reflect light and zones that absorb it and translates this information in sequences of 0 and 1.

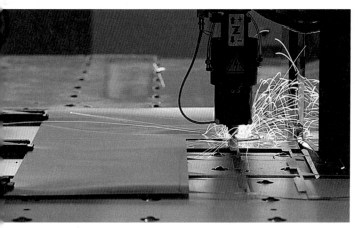

The laser
It is a light that is monochromatic (of only one color) and coherent (not dispersed in space but remaining concentrated in a beam). It is obtained by a kind of chain reaction within particular crystals.

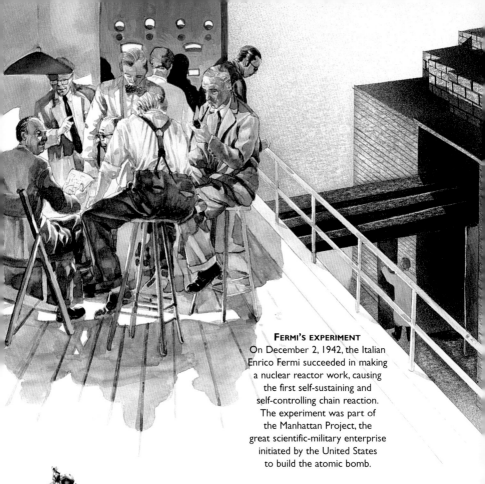

FERMI'S EXPERIMENT
On December 2, 1942, the Italian
Enrico Fermi succeeded in making
a nuclear reactor work, causing
the first self-sustaining and
self-controlling chain reaction.
The experiment was part of
the Manhattan Project, the
great scientific-military enterprise
initiated by the United States
to build the atomic bomb.

The other great innovation of twentieth-century technology is the potential to produce large quantities of goods for a great many people.

Along with innovations destined for manufacturing and large services, industry flooded the world with microinventions for individual use.

Energy

In 1900, coal was practically the only fuel used to produce energy. Within a few decades it popularity was threatened by other fossil fuels. In the United States, already in 1950, the consumption of oil and coal was equal. Burning coal or oil was and still is one of the most popular methods of generating energy. Alternative ways of generating energy included splitting the nuclei of atoms, as well as using hydroelectric power.

From the classical age, with the Greek philosopher Democritus (circa 460–380

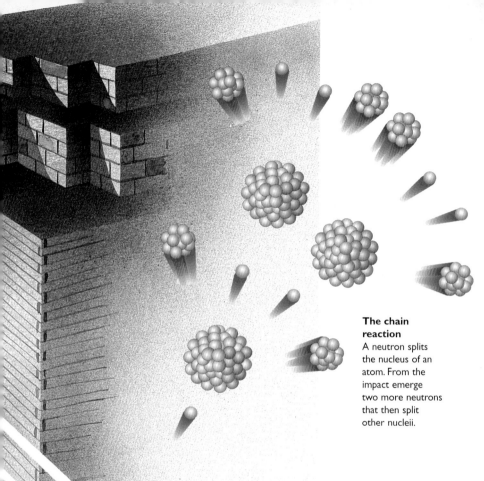

The chain reaction
A neutron splits the nucleus of an atom. From the impact emerge two more neutrons that then split other nucleii.

;.c.), until the twentieth century, the existence of an infinitesimally small and indivisible particle had been conceived of. Studies conducted between the end of the nineteenth and the beginning of the twentieth centuries, enhanced by the discovery of radioactivity and the electron, gave rise to hypotheses concerning the composition and structure of the atom, which, if properly understood, could be "split." Splitting an atom releases energy.

Nuclear energy was born in 1938, the year the German physicist Otto Hahn split in two the nucleus of a uranium atom, but it wasn't until 1942 when, stimulated by war-related needs, very large quantities of energy could be obtained from the atom. Released in an uncontrolled manner, atomic energy is destructive; in a controlled manner, on the other hand, it is capable of providing energy. The first nuclear plant for the production of electricity was built in

1956 at Calder Hall, in England. In subsequent years, nuclear fission was adopted by many nations, but it did not resolve, as was expected, the problem of increasing energy requirements.

A few incidents (the gravest was that of Chernobyl, in the Ukraine, on April 26, 1986) have alerted the world to the danger of nuclear power plants.

These concerns and those regarding the large quantities of carbon dioxide emitted into the atmosphere by burning coal and oil have stimulated the search for new forms of energy. In principle, the best solution would be to produce energy by means of nuclear fusion, the same process that fuels the sun. But the process is difficult to implement, and it is unlikely that the energy people consume in the immediate future will be a product of nuclear fusion. It is more likely to be produced by means of so-called renewable sources, that is, sources of energy that, unlike coal and oil, will not be depleted and do not pollute: wind, sun, rivers, and oceans.

Telecommunications

One of the earliest achievements of the 1900s is the radio. In 1901 Guglielmo Marconi successfully transmitted transatlantic radio signals. In 1906, in Massachusetts, two musical pieces and a brief speech were transmitted over hundreds of miles thanks to a new technique presented by the Canadian physicist Reginald A. Fassenden.

As a means of communication at a political, cultural, social, and economic level, the radio soon became more

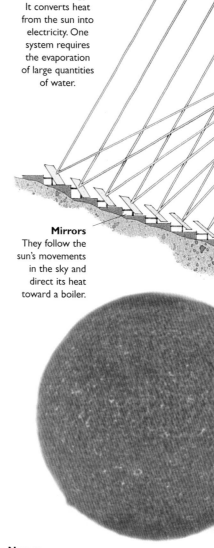

Solar energy
It converts heat from the sun into electricity. One system requires the evaporation of large quantities of water.

Mirrors
They follow the sun's movements in the sky and direct its heat toward a boiler.

NUCLEAR FUSION
By forcing two hydrogen atoms to fuse in order to make one of helium, a great amount of energy can be obtained without radioactive waste, as is the case with fission. It is the same principle that keeps the sun "burning."

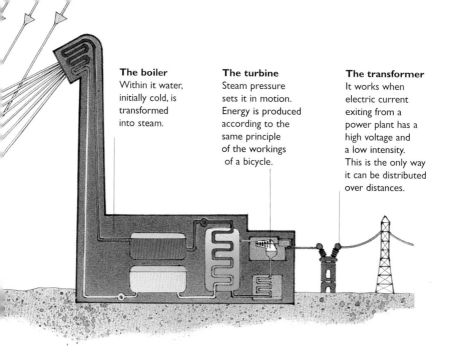

The boiler
Within it water, initially cold, is transformed into steam.

The turbine
Steam pressure sets it in motion. Energy is produced according to the same principle of the workings of a bicycle.

The transformer
It works when electric current exiting from a power plant has a high voltage and a low intensity. This is the only way it can be distributed over distances.

Aeolian power plants
They are modern windmills. They have gigantic blades (115 feet in diameter, on average) placed on towers 98 feet high.

important than printing because of its capacity to enter every home more easily.

During the 1920s television began to take shape, the result of a concept introduced in 1884 by the German Paul Nipkow: the conversion of an image in a series of lines consisting of points of different luminous intensity and its transmission via electromagnetic waves.

Still, it was only because of the contribution of many scientists and subsequent inventions such as the cathode tube, the radio, and the development of electronics that television technology became feasible. In 1907, Russian physicist Boris Rosing realized the cathode ray tube could receive images. In 1938 the first working television camera was produced, and a year later the first American public television service was started.

Televised programs remained at the experimental stage until the end of World War II and began to develop at the end of the 1940s, first in the United States and a few years later in European countries. After black and white television became popular, the technological development of color television began. Its commercial use in the United States was authorized in 1950, and three years later the first color programs were televised. The next step was TV via satellite. On July 10, 1962, Telstar I was launched, the first manmade satellite for telecommunications. A few days later, the worldwide telecast was born: thanks to Telstar, the first USA-Europe television link became a reality.

Since then there have been improvements large and small. Examples are the remote control, the videocassette recorder (VCR), and digital videodisc player

The cathode tube
Introduced in 1897, it is the heart of the television set— a glass bulb with a vacuum within it in which a beam of electrons travels.

THE FIRST TELEVISION
In 1926 the British engineer John L. Baird succeeded in producing a low-definition televised image (30 lines and 5 frames per second) by using a device introduced by Nipkow in 1884.

The television proliferates
By 1947 television sets that could be used in homes were already being produced, even though the first models, in black and white, were still rudimentary and there were few programs to watch.

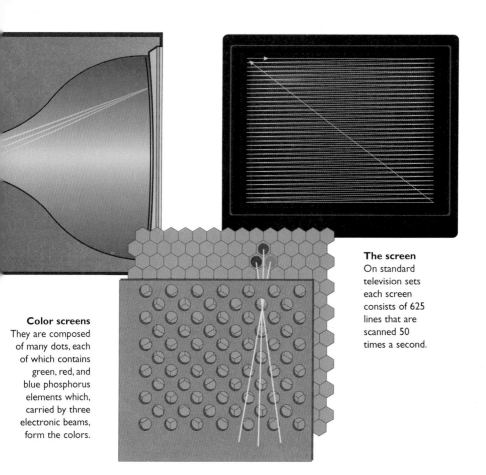

Color screens
They are composed of many dots, each of which contains green, red, and blue phosphorus elements which, carried by three electronic beams, form the colors.

The screen
On standard television sets each screen consists of 625 lines that are scanned 50 times a second.

(DVD). The next frontier will be interactive TV. The home televiewer will have access to enormous archives containing programs of every kind and linked to the television set by fiber optic cables.

Computer science

The first computer appeared in 1946. Produced by the American engineers John William Mauchly and John Prespert Eckart, ENIAC (acronym for *Electronic Numeral Integrator and Computer*) was the first computer that was com- pletely electronic and without mechanical moving parts. It was an enormous apparatus that occupied more than 1,500 square feet of floor space. It was developed for the U.S. Army, which used it to automatically compute ballistic statistics. The invention of the transistor, much more versatile and less cumbersome than the old vacuum tubes, soon rendered the ENIAC obsolete. By the end of the 1950s, second-generation computers appeared: small, inexpensive, efficient, and much more powerful.

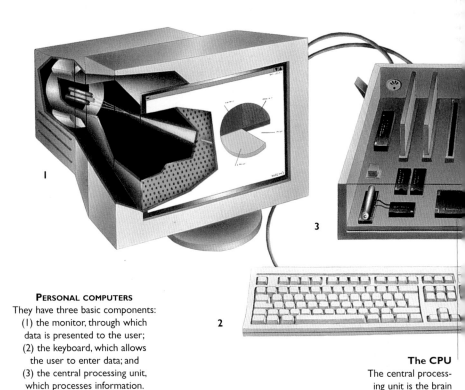

PERSONAL COMPUTERS
They have three basic components:
(1) the monitor, through which
data is presented to the user;
(2) the keyboard, which allows
the user to enter data; and
(3) the central processing unit,
which processes information.

The CPU
The central process-
ing unit is the brain
of the computer.

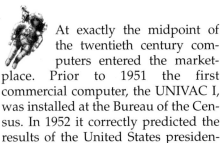

At exactly the midpoint of the twentieth century computers entered the marketplace. Prior to 1951 the first commercial computer, the UNIVAC I, was installed at the Bureau of the Census. In 1952 it correctly predicted the results of the United States presidential election. The following year a computer, based on the design of the British EDSAC computer of Cambridge University, was used to process orders for bread and sweets for J Lyons's chain of bakeries in London.

It was the computer's first commercial application. The demand for computers grew so rapidly that by the year 1960, 26 computer companies were already operating in the United States, seven in Great Britain, three in

RAM memory
The computer temporarily records information that it uses for a specific function or period of time.

The hard drive
It is an extensive electronic archive that stores information that must be saved for a long time.

The microprocessor
The first, invented in 1971, was a silicon plate about one inch wide and one and a half inches long on which the function of thousands of transistors were compressed.

Germany, two in the Netherlands, one in France, and one in Italy.

The brain of the modern computer, the microprocessor, was invented in 1971 by the Italian engineer Federico Fagin and by the Americans Todd Hoff and Stan Mazer. It was a decisive moment for the explosion of computer science. Computers were now powerful but small enough to sit on a desk.

The first personal computer in history was the Apple II, introduced by Steve Jobs and Steve Wozniak in 1977.

From a technological point of view, the 1990s will probably be remembered for the explosion of the phenomenal Internet and, in a broader sense, for the possibilities offered by the worldwide interconnection of millions of computers.

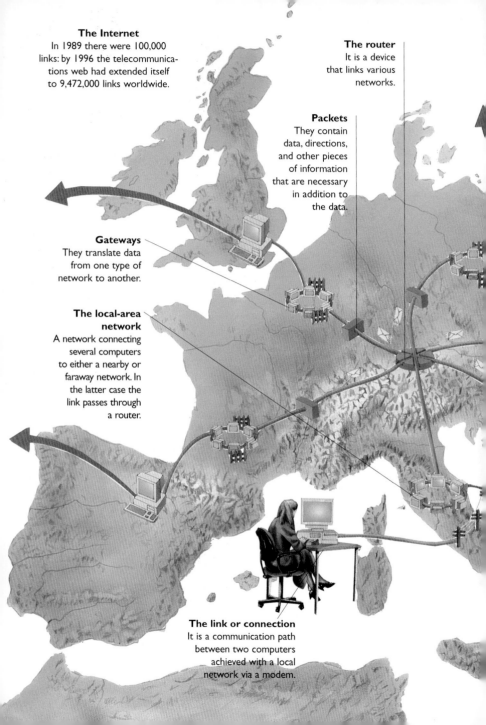

The Internet
In 1989 there were 100,000 links: by 1996 the telecommunications web had extended itself to 9,472,000 links worldwide.

The router
It is a device that links various networks.

Packets
They contain data, directions, and other pieces of information that are necessary in addition to the data.

Gateways
They translate data from one type of network to another.

The local-area network
A network connecting several computers to either a nearby or faraway network. In the latter case the link passes through a router.

The link or connection
It is a communication path between two computers achieved with a local network via a modem.

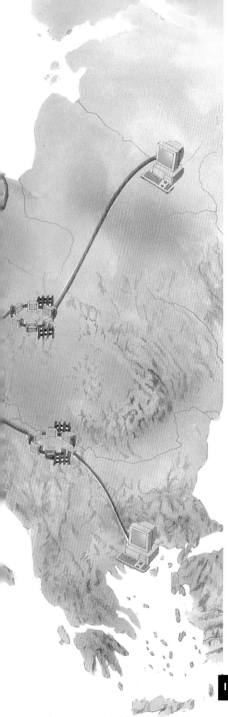

Even the Internet, like other innovations of the twentieth century, is the by-product of military research and competition between the United States and the Soviet Union. In the middle of the Cold War, Americans feared that the Soviets could sabotage the entire U.S. communications system. The solution was proposed by Paul Baran: it would be necessary to remove from each central power facility the network that linked the various nerve centers of the nation and render independent all the links, so that they would all have an equal hierarchical position and each would be capable of conceiving, transmitting, and receiving messages. Thus the embryo of the Arpanet network was born, enabling scientists and researchers, each possessing a personal electronic mail address, to exchange data and information.

The industry

The technology of the twentieth century has not only contributed to the invention of new machines but, by revolutionizing industrial production systems, has also permitted their widespread proliferation, making them available for everyone's use. The best example, as well as the first one in history, is that of the automobile.

In 1908, Henry Ford began production on his famous Model T. It was an automobile that perfectly fulfilled the new demand for mass consumer goods. Moreover, it was economically accessible to a large portion of the population.

The strong demand for the automobile prompted Henry Ford and his associates to modify their production system to devise a new kind of labor organization in their factories, one capable of accelerating production time. In the new factory the operators worked and performed a limited number of movements and tasks in relation to a specific phase of the finished product. Work was performed at well-designed lines and under the control of middle management employees, who were at an intermediate level between operators and directors on boards: it is the assembly line system of production, already in place by 1913. The new production process reduced the work time required to produce an automobile

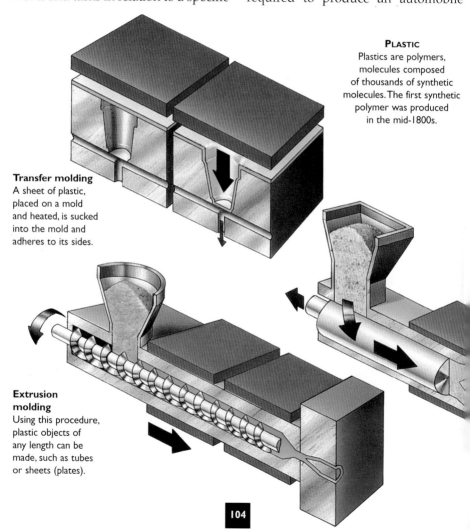

PLASTIC
Plastics are polymers, molecules composed of thousands of synthetic molecules. The first synthetic polymer was produced in the mid-1800s.

Transfer molding
A sheet of plastic, placed on a mold and heated, is sucked into the mold and adheres to its sides.

Extrusion molding
Using this procedure, plastic objects of any length can be made, such as tubes or sheets (plates).

from 12 hours and 8 minutes at the beginning of 1913 to 1 hour and 33 minutes by the spring of 1914.

The plant at Highland Park, Detroit, began to produce more than a thousand cars a day. The speed, volume, and efficiency, entirely unprecedented in industrial manufacturing, allowed Henry Ford to build the least expensive automobile in the world, to pay the highest salaries, and to become one of the wealthiest men in the world. The Ford factory applied Frederick Winslow Taylor's (1856–1915) theories on the scientific organization of labor. It was the result of an attempt to ease the industrial crisis of the late 1800s and stimulated a huge demand for new products from a growing number of consumers.

Compression molding
It is a technique that allows the production of plastic objects by means of the liquification and solidification of granulated polymers in a mold.

The assembly line
In the era of information science and technology, assembly lines are almost completely robotic.

The Empire State Building
It was completed in 1931 and at 1,250 feet high, it long remained the tallest building in the world.

Workers at work
The skyscrapers' steel structures were assembled by hundreds of workers. Many Native Americans were chosen for this work because of their agility and courage.

After World War II, particularly during the first 20 years of extraordinary economic growth, technological innovation increasingly produced successful market goods.

However, the development of new products incurred increasingly higher production costs, and research ac-

For the train only
The tunnel is only for railroad use. A central tunnel guarantees the timely arrival of rescue assistance.

The tunnel beneath the English Channel
The "Chunnel" was completed in 1993. Three tunnels more than 31 miles long link France and Great Britain. The cost was $1.5 billion.

counted for the largest percentage of these costs.

Buildings

Civil engineering underwent an important development during the first half of the twentieth century. All over the world, but especially in the United States, skyscrapers, bridges, and dams appeared. By the end of the 1800s structures of brick had reached their practical limit, and in cities such as Chicago and New York iron and steel skyscrappers replaced earlier buildings.

In order to build higher buildings it was necessary to wait until steel prices became more affordable and elevators became more reliable. All the major American cities became taller, taking advantage of the unlimited potential offered by new construction materials. In addition to steel, other materials appeared that permitted building large and imposing structures. Reinforced concrete had been patented in 1892, but only since the first decade of the twentieth century was it used in such a way as to revolutionize architecture. In 1928 the French engineer Marie Eugene Freyssinet tried out pre-stressed concrete for the first time—a minor revolution, because this material proved to be much more resistant than reinforced concrete and allowed the building of bridges with much longer spans.

In the second half of the century, machines that facilitated the work of builders in construction yards were

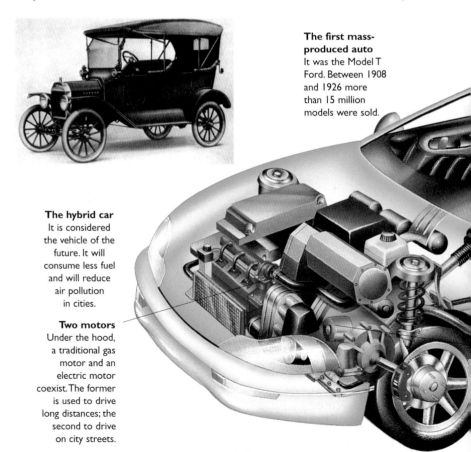

The first mass-produced auto
It was the Model T Ford. Between 1908 and 1926 more than 15 million models were sold.

The hybrid car
It is considered the vehicle of the future. It will consume less fuel and will reduce air pollution in cities.

Two motors
Under the hood, a traditional gas motor and an electric motor coexist. The former is used to drive long distances; the second to drive on city streets.

improved and made widely available: cranes, mechanical shovels, excavators, drills.

Such achievements also addressed the possibility of building structures underground. In the last ten years the real challenge for engineers and architects has not been skyscrapers but longer and wider tunnels.

Means of transportation

The automobile, as we have seen, became popular due to lower costs, the increased reliability, and improved highways. In the pioneer stages of the auto industry, manufacturers of automobiles underwent more radical changes than in any other period. But with the passage of time only the best ideas survived. In 1934, for example, the French engineer André Lefebvre produced the first automobile with front-wheel drive for Citroën. It was an innovation that increased both the stability and power of vehicles.

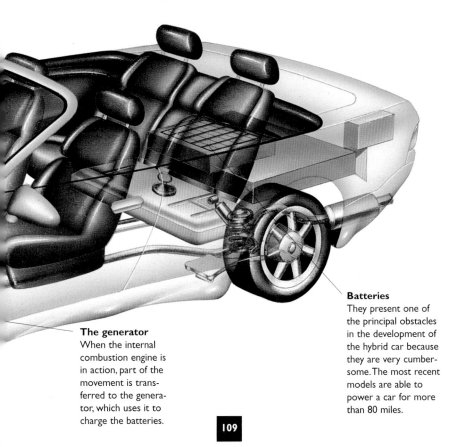

The generator
When the internal combustion engine is in action, part of the movement is transferred to the generator, which uses it to charge the batteries.

Batteries
They present one of the principal obstacles in the development of the hybrid car because they are very cumbersome. The most recent models are able to power a car for more than 80 miles.

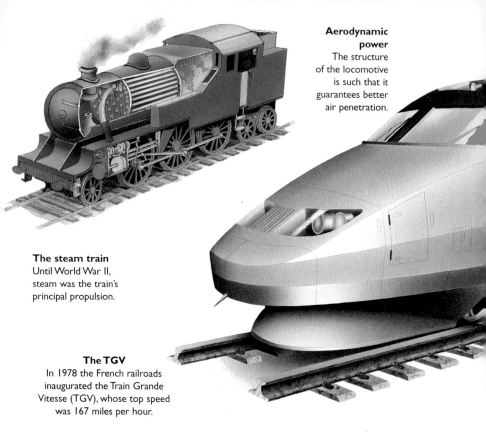

Aerodynamic power
The structure of the locomotive is such that it guarantees better air penetration.

The steam train
Until World War II, steam was the train's principal propulsion.

The TGV
In 1978 the French railroads inaugurated the Train Grande Vitesse (TGV), whose top speed was 167 miles per hour.

Automobiles are an amalgamation of technology. Even if their basic parts are not very different from those of the early twentieth-century models, electronics are more or less everywhere: from the fuel injection in the cylinders to the raising and lowering of electric windows. In addition, in recent times, inventors have committed themselves to constructing cars that are safer for passengers and less polluting to the environment. Seatbelts, antilocking or ABS brakes, and the airbag—the balloon that inflates in case of an accident to reduce the impact—are now available on most cars. An attempt was made to reduce the emission of polluting substances but, given the large number of cars in circulation, the measures taken are still insufficient. Many contend that the future will belong to hybrid cars half gas-burning, half electric.

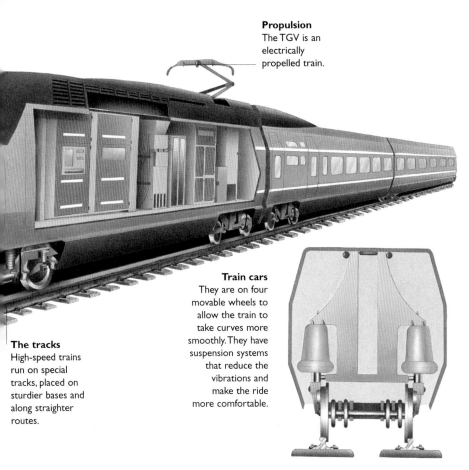

Propulsion
The TGV is an electrically propelled train.

The tracks
High-speed trains run on special tracks, placed on sturdier bases and along straighter routes.

Train cars
They are on four movable wheels to allow the train to take curves more smoothly. They have suspension systems that reduce the vibrations and make the ride more comfortable.

One form of electric transportation that is now common is the train. The first electric railroad in the world was the miniature line built to transport visitors within the Berlin Exhibition of 1879, but it was only after World War II that people relied on electricity to drive trains. The achievements that followed were more concerned with speed and safety than with propulsion systems.

Magnetic levitation trains is a completely different technology. The repellent force between magnets of opposite poles keeps the trains raised from the tracks, thereby eliminating the force of friction. The combination of attractions and repulsions then forces the train to advance. The first prototype of its kind was tried out in the United States in 1967 and proved very promising.

In 1976 Germany produced the Transrapid, capable of traveling at 249 miles an hour, and in 1980 the Japanese Magnetic Levitation Train reached a speed of 320 miles per hour. Despite these results, the magnetic levitation train is still far from becoming a commercial reality.

Aviation

The first flight dates to 1903, and the airplane almost immediately became a weapon, used by the Italians for the first time in their war against the Turks in Libya in 1911.

In the years between the first and second World War, the fragile biplanes of the aviation pioneers were replaced by

The first flight
In 1903 Orville Wright flew his plane above a flat, sandy field for just 12 seconds, covering a distance of almost 131 feet at a speed of approximately 30 miles per hour. His apparatus was a simple biplane without a tail, with a propulsion propeller powered by a 12-horsepower gas motor.

The Osaka Airport
The air terminal of Osaka International Airport, in Japan, stands on an artificial island. It was completed in 1994 based on the design of the Italian architect Renzo Piano.

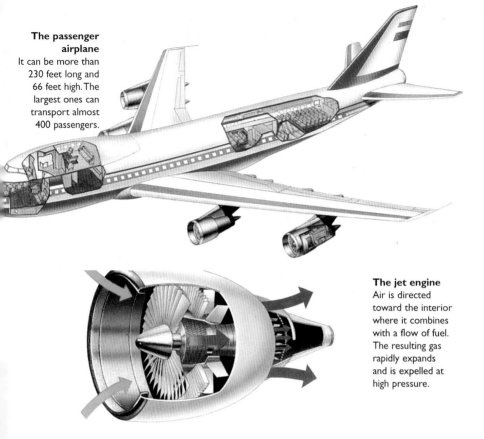

The passenger airplane
It can be more than 230 feet long and 66 feet high. The largest ones can transport almost 400 passengers.

The jet engine
Air is directed toward the interior where it combines with a flow of fuel. The resulting gas rapidly expands and is expelled at high pressure.

sturdy monoplanes that flew along intercontinental routes.

On August 27, 1939, the first jet plane took flight. Its motor, patented by the Englishman Frank Whittle, was revolutionary. It took in air and then expelled it with very great pressure. This jet was the prototype for airplanes today.

The conquest of space

Man also learned how to conquer gravity to go into space. Stimulated by the pressure of the Cold War, the United States and the Soviet Union dedicated themselves to designing ever more powerful rockets, capable of transporting atomic bombs from one continent to another. Studies in this field had already been carried out by the Germans during the Second World War and had produced the deadly "flying rockets," the famous V1 and V2, that the Germans dropped on London at the end of the war. On October 4, 1957, the Soviet Union launched Sputnik I into orbit. It was a steel sphere carrying on board instruments to measure the temperature and density of the atmosphere.

THE SPACE STATION

It will be the greatest scientific venture of the next few years. Scholars from all over the world will be able to conduct their experiments in the absence of gravity, within the structure that will orbit the Earth.

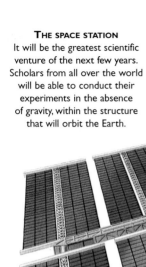

The *Columbus*
A laboratory in which experiments will be conducted in physical science, the physics of fluids, and biology.

Links
They will connect the various modules and allow the astronauts to pass from module to module.

The first man on the moon
"That's one small step for man, one giant leap for mankind." These were the first words uttered by Neil Armstrong as he set foot on the moon on July 21, 1969.

The shuttles
The shuttles, operational since 1981, guaranteed the piece-by-piece assembly of the space station.

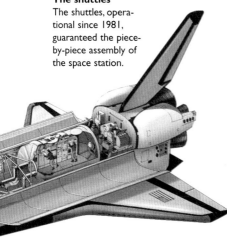

The LEM
It was the Lunar Excursion Module that brought Armstrong, Aldrin, and Collins to the moon's surface. Two hours before landing it had detached from the *Columbia*, which remained in orbit circling the moon.

The following month, on November 3, Sputnik II was launched. It weighed 1120 pounds, seven pounds of which were scientific instruments. Also on board was the first living being ever to go into space, the dog Laika. On April 12, 1961, Soviet space engineering achieved its zenith when it launched into orbit aboard the capsule *Vostok* the cosmonaut Yuri Gagarin, the first man to reach space. It took a few years for the United States to catch up to the Soviets, but it decisively assumed the lead in the conquest of space. On July 20, 1969, thanks to a rocket invented by Wernher von Braun, the United States sent the astronauts Neil Armstrong, Edwin Aldrin, and Michael Collins to the moon and successfully brought them back safe and sound.

Technology and war

Radar, missiles, artificial satellites, and the Internet are all systems that came about directly or indirectly from the military.

The first obvious example of the military's involvement with a scientist or with an entire research facility was demonstrated by Fritz Haber. During the First World War, the German chemist—who would eventually win the Nobel Prize for being the first to synthesize ammonia—managed to equip the German army with propellants and explosives such as nitroglycerine, nitrocellulose, and trinitrotoluene (TNT).

It was the first large-scale use of synthetic chemical substances for military purposes. But Haber went even further and set out to find a lethal gas that could be used on battlefields. He proposed using chlorine, a powerful asphyxiating gas, in liquid form that upon contact with air evaporates, forming a low-altitude cloud. Much more devastating weapons of destruction have been invented since. For the entire period of the Cold War, thousands of nuclear warhead missiles had been aimed at principal cities in the U.S.S.R. and the United States. The atomic destruction inflicted on the Japanese cities of Hiroshima and Nagasaki in August of 1945 had, however, dissuaded the great powers from setting off a nuclear war that would culminate in the destruction of both victim and aggressor.

Currently, military strategy anticipates the enemy's actions and aims at striking its nerve centers rather than annihilation. For this reason stealth airplanes and smart missiles have been developed. In some American aviation laboratories, robots instead of human beings are made to pilot the airplanes.

Life-saving technology

Technology can bring benefits as well as destruction. The majority of medicines used to cure people, for example, did not exist a century ago. In the 1900s research and pharmaceutical industries had transformed themselves: the experience of a good herbalist no longer sufficed to synthesize a medicine. The scientific knowledge of chemists and doctors and the technological means provided by large laboratories were needed.

The best example of a medical advance is aspirin, which, even though it was first offered in 1897, completely belongs to twentieth-century medicine. Other important pre-1900 medical advances are: the development of the smallpox vaccine by Englishman Edward Jenner

GASES
In April of 1915, during World War I, the Germans dropped 6,000 bombs containing liquid chlorine on the Western Front, killing 5,000 men. The attacks then proceeded to the Russian Front, where the gas left approximately 25,000 dead or injured men on the fields.

THE ATOMIC BOMB
Dropped on Hiroshima on August 6, 1945, it had the effect of 15,000 tons of trinitrotoluene (TNT) as it razed 3.8 square miles of the city to the ground, killing 66,000 people instantly and injuring another 69,000.

in the late 1700s; an injection to prevent rabies from developing and pasteurization by Frenchman Louis Pasteur in the 1800s; and the X-ray by German Wilhelm Roentgen in the late 1800s.

Penicillin, discovered in 1928 by Alexander Fleming, was the salvation for millions of people afflicted with infectious illnesses. Another important date for twentieth-century medicine is April 26, 1954: on that day the United States instituted a mass vaccination program against poliomyelitis, a virus that in the United States alone paralyzed 20,000 people each year. Different versions of the vaccine were prepared independently by the biochemist Jonas Salk and the microbiologist Albert Sabin.

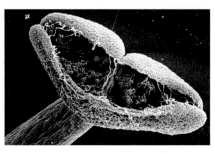

An enlargement
The final portion of a flower's stamen with the relative pollen granules.

The electron microscope
It uses a beam of electrons in place of light. The traditional glass lenses are replaced by magnetic fields. Those of the most recent generation can photograph the individual atoms that make up matter.

MASS VACCINATIONS
Vaccination campaigns, including the one against polio, put into effect after World War II have saved thousands of lives. Entire populations are now immune, especially in developing countries, from the most dreadful diseases.

Organ transplants, which have been made possible by the introduction of anti-rejection drugs as well as the increased ability of surgeons, are another example of technological success applied to medicine. In 1954, the American surgeon Joseph Murray performed the first kidney transplant. Two years later the hematologist E. Donnal Thomas transplanted healthy bone marrow in a leukemia patient. In 1963 the first liver and lung transplants were performed. Finally, on December 3, 1967 the South African surgeon Christiaan Barnard performed the first heart transplant.

Diagnostics is probably the field of medicine where technology has had its most resounding impact. Complex machines, taking advantage of the various laws of physics, succeed in photographing the entire human body; among them is computerized axial tomography (CAT), used for the first time in 1972. CAT scans combine the radiographic (X-ray) method with a computer reconstruction and allow a view of the patient's body as if it had been sliced and then photographed.

The structure of DNA
It was identified for the first time in 1953 by Francis Crick and James Watson. For this discovery, they won the Nobel Prize for Medicine in 1962.

Genetic engineering

It is considered by many to be the technology of the future, one that could save human lives and allow the production of new foods. It was born with the discovery of DNA, that is, the molecule that contains all the information necessary to "construct" a living being, and an understanding of the mechanisms by which this information is transmitted. The code to decipher this structure was identified in 1953, opening the doors to genetics and to the possibility of modifying the genetic traits of living beings. Genetic engineering demonstrated its capacity for diagnosis for the first time in 1976, when a technique capable of making an early diagnosis of alpha-thalassemia was introduced at the University of San Francisco. From then, different links to DNA have been utilized for the diagnosis of genetic illnesses. In the 1980s, in addition to diagnosis, the future of gene therapy—curing genetic illnesses at the DNA level—became increasingly plausible, in other words,

CLONING
It is one of the most recent, and most controversial, achievements of genetic engineering: creating an animal that is identical to another mature one.

The egg cell
It is drawn from another sheep.

The sheep to be cloned
One of its cells is drawn.
The genetic code contained
in the nucleus of the cell
faithfully describes the
animal's characteristics.

In the uterus
The new egg cell
is made to take
root in the uterus
of a third sheep.

The birth
The lamb that is
born is a perfect
clone of the
original sheep.

The transfer
The nucleus of the
cell of the sheep
to be cloned, and
therefore its genetic
code, is transferred
to an egg cell.

DNA
The American Oswald Avery
was the first to demonstrate
that it was the molecule of
life. While studying bacteria,
he verified that every trait of
an individual was written in
the long DNA molecules.

the "substitution" of defective genes
with "normal" ones.

The first attempt on a human being
dates to 1990. The Americans W. French
Anderson and Michael Blaese drew
some white blood cells from a sick girl
and returned them to her body after
having introduced a missing gene.

The most recent experiments, for
example, the cloning of the sheep Dolly
that occurred in 1997, have demonstrated that scientists now truly know how to
penetrate the genetic makeup and modify the characteristics of living beings.

Index

The numbers in italics refer to items discussed in the captions.